A

Depression?

***

Hint: You May Have Undiagnosed ADD or PTSD

***

Jeffrey H. Pinsk, MD

Anxiety?
Depression?

Hint: You May Have Undiagnosed ADD or PTSD

ISBN 978-1-7341242-0-0
LCCN: 2019916261

***

Dedication

This book is dedicated to my patients, past, present, and future, whom I've had the privilege to care for and learn from. And to my family, whom I have been privileged to learn from and to care for. You know who you are....

J. P.

Table of Contents

Introduction

I have been a physician for over thirty years, and a student of human nature for my entire life. From my earliest days in medicine, many patients seeking help for anxiety, depression, or substance abuse have shared their stories with me, often helping to reveal the root cause of their condition. I have felt compelled to share these stories with colleagues, anonymously, because they were too fascinating to keep to myself! Now, I hope to share some of these stories with you.

Over the course of my many years in family practice, I have come to recognize patterns of behavior in my patients that have not been adequately described or explained in medical textbooks, journals, or lectures. Conditions such as anxiety, depression, alcoholism, and substance abuse, are misunderstood by medical and mental health professionals. In the majority of patients, these are symptoms of an underlying condition, not the root cause of their illness.

Frequently, post-traumatic stress disorder (PTSD) or attention deficit disorder (ADD) is the underlying cause of the anxiety, depression, and addiction. Since many professionals are treating the symptoms of anxiety and depression instead of the PTSD or ADD that is causing those symptoms, it should be no surprise that so many people are not getting better. By recognizing and embracing the root causes of anxiety and depression, I have put into practice the principles and the treatment of what I have learned over the course of my career with amazing and life changing results for many of my patients.

Normal Anxiety

Situational anxiety and depression occur in everyone at some point in their lives. I call this 'normal'. Our mood is altered by life's challenges—a death in the family, the breakup of a relationship, the loss of a job, financial difficulties, being a teenager, or being the parent of a teenager! Many people need medication and psychotherapy to help them cope with the anxious and depressed mood that comes with these challenges. Furthermore, some anxiety and depression are hereditary. There is a chemical imbalance in the brain that runs in the family and is in their DNA. The neurotransmitters serotonin, dopamine, norepinephrine, and others are over-or underproduced by the neurons in the brain, creating chronic anxiety and depression without an obvious situational or underlying cause.

Abnormal Anxiety

I have written this book for the majority of people who are anxious and depressed but do not have either situational or hereditary anxiety or depression. It is my assertion that you may have underlying and undiagnosed PTSD or ADD. Your response may be, "How could I have PTSD or ADD? I have a responsible job, a spouse, children, and a mortgage." My answer is that although you're successful, you are still troubled by your past emotional traumas. You think that they're in the past and resolved. However, your symptoms of anxiety and depression tell me that these are not scars—they are unresolved, open wounds. You revisit them many days and most nights when you obsess about the past and worry about the future. This worrying is toxic and only known to you, not to others around you.

As an analogy, we all know functioning alcoholics who go to work every day and seem to have stable family lives. That person may not even consider themselves to be an alcoholic! Like all conditions and diseases, PTSD and ADD can be very mild in comparison to the more severe and obvious cases that we all recognize. You might think that the homeless veteran living on the street in the city has PTSD, and you wouldn't be wrong. However, you wouldn't realize that your neighbor, who is a nice person and has a family, a mortgage, and a responsible job just like you also has PTSD. The symptoms of illness are often much less obvious and much more subtle in most patients and for most conditions. That's why doctors have to go to medical school, and why we 'practice' medicine!

It is essential to make the correct diagnosis in order to prescribe the appropriate treatment. For example, if you diagnose someone with a fever and treat them with Tylenol, you will miss the true underlying diagnosis of strep throat, and you won't prescribe penicillin. The end result will be that they feel better from the Tylenol, but they won't get better because they didn't receive the antibiotic. If you make the wrong diagnosis, you'll prescribe inadequate treatment. Welcome to the problem with mental health care. Many times, we are making the wrong diagnosis and are administering the wrong treatment. Until professionals recognize that we are missing the underlying PTSD or ADD that is causing your depression or anxiety, improvement is likely to be temporary or incomplete.

Furthermore, therapists have been taught and trained to start at the present and work backward. Many of you who have undergone psychotherapy will have had this experience. You start at the end, your current symptoms, and work towards the beginning, your childhood. There is a major problem with this strategy: You get stuck! You never get back to the beginning. We medical professionals must change our approach to psychotherapy. We need to start at the beginning, the past, and work forward, to the present.

A New Approach

Childhood, adolescence, and young adulthood are where major emotional traumas most often occur. Today's emotional distress follows a well-worn pattern of anxiety and depression that has been present for years or perhaps decades. To understand your emotions today, we need to first examine your childhood, at your very first visit. This is a radical concept and would be considered heresy in the mental health community today. However, the current approach to mental health is working poorly. Studies tell us that almost seven million adults in our country have chronic Generalized Anxiety Disorder. Another six million adults have Panic Disorder, and sixteen million have Major Depressive Disorder, including three million depressed patients who have chronic, persistent depression. We need a new and fundamentally different approach to psychiatry and psychotherapy.

I like to think of the DSM-V manual in terms of the Hindu parable of the blind men and the elephant. A teacher asks seven blind men to describe an elephant. Each man takes a different part of the elephant and describes, in great detail, their findings. One describes the tusk; another, the trunk; another, the tail; etc. Because they are blind, none of the men see that their experience is just a part of the whole. In my analogy, PTSD and ADD are the elephant; anxiety and depression are the trunk and the tail.

We need your help. We need you to go to your therapist and tell them, "I think that I have PTSD (or ADD) causing my symptoms of anxiety (or depression)." In this way, you will target the focus of your therapy where it belongs—at the beginning. You can then explore, with your therapist, how and why your current emotional distress is caused by your past emotional trauma. Instead of spending time and money looking for the answer to the question "Why am I anxious?" or "Why am I depressed?", give your therapist the answer so that you can start treatment immediately.

Chapter 1: What are Anxiety and Depression?

We all feel anxious at times—during a job interview, taking a math test, or going to the doctor's office. In these types of situations, we are thinking about the past and worrying about the future. "Will I get the job?" "Will I pass the exam?" "Will the doctor find cancer?" We are both consciously and unconsciously thinking negative thoughts, which create negative feelings, and which lead to physical consequences.

When we're anxious, stress hormones, such as adrenaline, cortisol, and growth hormone, are created in the brain. These hormones cause the heart rate and blood pressure to rise, causing a stronger and more rapid pulse, which may cause palpitations. The muscles tighten, including the chest wall muscles, which can result in chest pain. The hands tremor, the heat in the body rises, and we sweat. Our breathing accelerates and we start to hyperventilate. This leads to an alkalosis in the blood chemistry making us feel lightheaded and dizzy. We panic: Could it be a heart attack?

We all feel depressed at times as well. Our mood dampens in response to a stressful life event that leads to negative or unpleasant consequences. We react to a death in the family, a loss of a job, or the breakup of a relationship. There are feelings of sadness, lack of pleasure, low energy, or no motivation. We avoid other people and our normal activities, choosing instead to be alone with our pain. These negative thoughts and feelings lead to the release of hormones by the brain that are different than those released when you are anxious. When you are depressed, dopamine is released and serotonin is inhibited, slowing the heart rate, breathing, and metabolism. You feel like you weigh a thousand pounds. It takes all your energy just to get dressed. Everything is a supreme effort, and nothing is pleasurable. You don't smile, laugh, or have any fun doing the things that you previously enjoyed. If this sounds familiar, you are not alone.

It is clear that anxiety and depression can be the natural and appropriate brain response to adverse circumstances. Psychiatrists call this an 'Adjustment Disorder.' It is a normal reaction that all of us experience, whether or not we seek medical or psychological help to manage the anxiety or depression. Similarly, some people have an inherited variety of anxiety and/or depression. For them, their brain chemistry is off-balance. Their DNA causes their brains to make more or less of the neurotransmitters, the hormones that cause anxiety and depression. These people have been anxious or depressed for as long as they can remember. Some of their siblings, parents, and extended members of the family may also suffer from anxiety and depression that is not situational. Those who have inherited anxiety or depression require life-long medication to correct the chemical imbalance in their brains. For them, antidepressants are like blood pressure medicine for people who have familial hypertension.

Situational Anxiety and Depression

Anxiety is the result of thinking about the past and worrying about the future. While this is important on an intellectual and rational level, it is counterproductive on an emotional level. As responsible adults, we need to plan our days, weeks, and months in order to successfully accomplish our work and family obligations. The only way to do this is to plan for the future—whether for work, travel, children's soccer games, or our parents' doctor appointments. However, when we look too far into the future on an emotional, existential basis, we scare ourselves because of the magnitude of the task or the uncertainty of the outcome.

If you are a hiker or mountain climber, it is daunting to look at the top when you are on the bottom. The key to success is to look up one level at a time so that you do not get overwhelmed. The same is true in life. If you are the parent of young children and already worried about where they are going to college and how you are going to pay for it, you will have a lot of unnecessary sleepless nights! It seems like an impossible task. We create our own anxiety by worrying and thinking too far ahead. We need to consciously and rationally force ourselves back to the present where we live on a daily basis.

Children are happy because yesterday never happened and tomorrow will never come. We need to be more childlike if we are making ourselves anxious by looking too far into the future. We need to focus and enjoy the challenges and pleasures of day-to-day life to avoid unnecessary anxiety caused by worrying about the future. We get from one place to another one step at a time, placing one foot in front of the other. If we focus on doing the best we can each day, and making the best decisions we can based on the information available at the time, we can avoid looking backwards with regret.

Unrealistic Expectations

Another frequent cause of anxiety and depression is having too many preconceived notions about how life 'should' be. "I should weigh 120 pounds." "I should be making more money." "I should be married by now." The list is endless. It is important to have goals, but it can be devastating to have expectations if they are artificial and unrealistic. Not everyone can be a professional athlete, musician, or actor. Not everyone is going to be a millionaire or have children who go to Ivy League schools. Not everyone is going to go to, or finish, college. Hope for the best, but you better have a 'plan B.'

Our societal expectations in today's environment are unrealistic and defy the facts of life and human nature. To many people under seventy years old, even death is optional! If someone dies, something must have gone wrong in the medical system. We are so focused on 'how we are doing' that we have forgotten 'what we are doing' and 'why we are doing it'. It is no wonder that in the most prosperous and advanced period of humanity, in the most prosperous country in the world, there is anxiety and depression. We need to temper our expectations.

When I graduated high school in 1976, we were excited about opportunities. We may have had lofty goals, but our expectations were modest: Find a good job, raise a family, and lead a comfortable life. Today, the expectations of many graduates and their parents is to make $100,000 per year by the time they are thirty, drive a BMW, and live in a McMansion. Remember, I said expectations, not goals. Even if they somehow manage to accomplish their goals, they don't feel good about their accomplishments because they are expected! That is the difference between goals and expectations. Goals are best-case outcomes, a potentially obtainable result to be aimed for, an 'A' if you will. However, if you expect an 'A,' anything else is a failure. Talk about anxiety…. In fact, in many high schools and colleges today, you can score over 100 percent, over a 4.0, over an 'A+'. Is it any wonder that young people and their parents are anxious?

We parents need to have an honest conversation with ourselves, our spouses, and our children in order to change our way of thinking about our goals versus expectations. In today's world, we are creating anxiety about the future, which will be self-fulfilling. We fear that we will not meet our expectations. That fear causes anxiety and prevents us from focusing on what is necessary to achieve our goals. Our performance suffers and causes us to become more anxious. Not surprisingly, the outcome is failure to meet our expectations and goals, which can easily lead to depression. Fear causes anxiety; anxiety inhibits our performance; and our underperformance creates more anxiety. If we keep repeating this paradigm, the likely result is depression. We need to be honest and realistic about what is possible, what is likely, and what is truly important. We need to be aware of our individual strengths and weaknesses, and the world in which we live. We adults and parents should feel good about what we have accomplished. We need to teach our children, by example, that the path to avoiding unnecessary stress and anxiety is to have realistic expectations, even if one has lofty goals.

Let's Gain Some Perspective

Winston Churchill said that those who forget history are doomed to repeat it. Not only have we forgotten history, but we have deemed it irrelevant! Literally. History class is no longer mandatory in many high schools and colleges—it is an optional elective. What history teaches us is perspective and context. If you see the world and life in the isolated time frame of only the present, you will overestimate life's shortcomings and underestimate historical achievements. Every problem and challenge in the present can seem overwhelming and monumental and could lead to Armageddon!

Before I graduated high school in 1976, our country dealt with the Vietnam War, the Kennedy assassinations, the Civil Rights movement, the Martin Luther King assassination, Watergate, and Richard Nixon—to name just a few of the more challenging events of the time. Then we experienced the Arab Oil Embargo and 19 percent inflation. And in 2001, Osama Bin Laden struck. Yet in the current time of relative peace and prosperity, it seems that we feel more anxious about the future than ever before. Why? We have become the victims of our own success! We have lost our perspective by intentionally forgetting where we have come from. We have forgotten our history. We should put today's problems and challenges into a historical perspective of other periods in our country's history and the world's history.

There will always be problems and challenges that need to be addressed. However, our technical achievements over the past twenty years have been astounding—with robotics, the internet, and the entire digital age. The previous fifty years were no less astounding—space travel, color television, and modern medicine. The Ken Burns series, *The Roosevelts*, reminded me that President FDR died of a cerebral hemorrhage in 1945 because there was no medicine for hypertension at that time. None. Unthinkable. Prior to 150 years ago, the only way to travel was by horse or ship. The Industrial Age brought us trains, automobiles, electricity, and telephones. It's no wonder that today we think death is optional! Everything 'should' be possible; anything else is failure. The result: Anxiety.

Human Nature

We also need to be honest and realistic about human nature. In a world that strives to be 'evidence based' and binary, we do not acknowledge human nature because we cannot measure it in any meaningful way. While the way we lead our daily lives has changed dramatically over time, human nature has not. How do we know? History. Read about our founding fathers and life in their times. Read Shakespeare, Aristotle, and the Bible. Human beings are jealous, greedy, vengeful, fearful, and completely fallible. Yet we live in a society where we are actually proud to have 'zero tolerance'! Being human and making mistakes is not tolerated, and the punishment for doing so far outweighs the crime. We have to be perfect or face the possibility of severe consequences. The result? Anxiety. The fear of making a mistake. The fear of doing something wrong or doing it the wrong way.

One of the common attributes of successful and famous people throughout history is their ingenuity and creativity. They have been the leaders in their fields because they have gone against the traditional establishment by being different and thinking outside of the box. Today, in education and most professions, independent thinking is frowned upon, discouraged, and severely punished. We ignore the fact that every individual is unique and is a product of their genetic makeup and life experiences. Instead of embracing our differences and learning about them and from them, we prefer to live in a world where human beings are interchangeable—they are all the same. There is only one right answer. There is only one way to do things. There is no dialogue, discussion, or exchange of ideas. We reject open-mindedness, empathy, and extenuating circumstances. 'One size fits all', with no exceptions. Is this really how we want to live? Being 'different' may make you anxious, if you truly believe that everyone else is the same.

Depression

Depression can stem from chronic anxiety, or from the failure to repeatedly meet expectations. It is exhausting to continuously worry about whether you are good enough. You continue to do what is comfortable and familiar to avoid taking risks, because taking risks is anxiety-provoking. You are bored, unchallenged, unfulfilled, and ultimately depressed. While you are stuck in a rut, the world keeps changing. The job that you were comfortable with when you started has changed. The children that you enjoyed when they were young have become teenagers. Your parents' health is deteriorating. Your spouse is not the same person they were when you first married. How did this happen, and how do I get out of it? Many people will do something destructive at this point, like having an affair.

The midlife crisis is very real. "Is this all life is about?" "Can I live this way for the rest of my life?" " My life is half over, and I feel like I am missing so much". Instead of doing something destructive, now is the time to take stock of your life and put it on a path to make sure that the next chapters of your life are more fulfilling. You may require some counseling and medication in order to help you. Don't be afraid and don't let your depression linger. Now is the time to seek professional help.

If you have situational anxiety or depression, or if you are contributing to your emotional distress by focusing on unrealistic expectations, you will likely benefit from medication and psychotherapy. However, for many people, anxiety and depression are long-standing and unexplainable. It is for you that I have written this book.

When Anxiety and Depression are Symptoms of Something Else

What are the underlying causes of anxiety and depression when situational or hereditary sources are not the answer? You may say to yourself, "My life is good. I have a good job. I have a caring spouse. I have normal, healthy children. I don't have any serious financial or health problems. Why am I unhappy?" In many cases, it is undiagnosed ADD or PTSD.

Many people have mild cases of ADD or PTSD and have reached adulthood without even realizing it. They live 'normal' lives until they hit a wall. I have seen this so many times in various forms. A good student in high school can't perform in college because of mild ADD. They procrastinate, have difficulty with organization, and have a hard time focusing in class and on their homework.

This causes anxiety which, affects their performance, which creates even more anxiety. They get depressed. They may drop out, or hopefully, seek medical attention. Their family physician or psychotherapist will recognize their anxiety or depression and order medication and therapy. However, too often the focus will be on the anxiety and depression, without exploring the root cause of their symptoms: Mild ADD.

An adult in their thirties may suddenly become depressed for no obvious reason. Everything is going well—job, spouse, kids. Certainly, there are everyday life stresses, but nothing new or different from last year. What is going on? What has changed? The answer may be that your unresolved PTSD has risen up in your level of subconscious. You have worked hard to achieve your goals and position in life by focusing on your work, your marriage, and your children. Now that your life is more stable and less dynamic, you don't have to focus as much on the day-to-day details. This allows the mind to wander and worry about the future.

You are constantly scanning for danger, looking over your shoulder, and waiting for something to come out of the blue and destroy all that you have created. You can't allow yourself to be happy because that will only make you more vulnerable to disappointment. The more you have, the more that you have to lose. You may have mild PTSD from an event in your past that was life-changing, such as a death in the family, or your parents' divorce when you were young. Your PTSD may be from having been bullied at school or verbally abused at home. You were constantly in imminent danger that was unprovoked, unforeseen, and unavoidable. Try as you may, you could not protect yourself—day after day. This made you anxious and insecure.

In the chapters that follow, I invite you to ask yourselves if you might have undiagnosed ADD or PTSD causing your anxiety or depression. If you think that you might be suffering from either, I encourage you to discuss it with your family physician or psychotherapist. Don't wait for them to figure it out without your input. We medical professionals have not realized the prevalence and extent of ADD and PTSD that affect those individuals who have managed to function 'normally' until they hit a wall. You may have a mild form of ADD or PTSD that you have been compensating for until now. We will explore ADD and PTSD in the following chapters to see if the diagnosis may apply to you.

Chapter 2: How the Brain Works

Psychology is based on neurology. Our 'personality', thoughts, feelings, memories, and decisions are all a function of physical and chemical actions and reactions in the brain. Neurons are nerve cells that make up the brain's physical structure. These neurons communicate with each other by releasing chemicals (neurotransmitters) that cause reactions in the adjacent nerve cells. Hence, our 'psychological' makeup is a function of the creation of neuronal connections, and by the chemicals produced by the individual neurons.

Psychology is not as confusing and nebulous as is commonly believed. We are all born with similar but slightly different brains that then develop as we learn. If we use a computer analogy, we are born with the hardware which has basic, preinstalled programs. With each new experience, we add new programs. And with repeated experiences, we reinforce and add data to these programs. The nerve pathways are traveled infinite numbers of times as the brain develops. Connections between nerve cells and between different areas of the brain are established. Eventually, these connections become almost automatic, i.e., subconscious. We don't think about them. For example, do you think about how to walk, or do you just start walking? Do you think about how to eat, or only about what to eat? My point is that thoughts and feelings are processed in a similar way and become automatic.

Conceptually, there is the conscious part of the brain and then the rest of the brain, the subconscious. The conscious part is the rational, thinking part of the brain that resides in the prefrontal cortex. This is the part of the brain where thoughts are generated, decisions are made, and volitional action is initiated—the 'executive functions' of the brain. In our computer analogy, it is our RAM. However, most of the brain activity is not initiated by, and does not involve, the executive function area of the brain. The RAM is just a fraction of the space and function on a computer. Similarly, the conscious part of the brain is just a small fraction of the brain; the rest of the functioning brain is subconscious.

Connectivity

We live in an era of specialization, especially in medicine. As such, we seem to have forgotten the most fundamental fact of human existence: Our thoughts, feelings, and actions are all integrated and directly related to each other. Our thoughts can affect our emotions, our emotions can affect our thoughts, and both can affect the conscious and unconscious actions of the body. It is essential to keep this premise in mind in order to correctly diagnose and treat patients with emotional and physical problems. Yet we have lost sight of the forest through the trees. Many medical professionals treat diseases or illnesses rather than treat human beings. We see parts of the patient, but we frequently don't see the whole person.

In my practice, I see patients each week who have physical manifestations of emotional distress. They have fibromyalgia, TMJ syndrome, or irritable bowel syndrome. They come to my office because they have headaches, muscle and joint pain, or abdominal pain with diarrhea and constipation. These are physical symptoms of medical conditions caused by emotional distress. In fibromyalgia, patients clench their bodies in their sleep as they process their stress. In TMJ syndrome, they grind their teeth and clench their jaws during sleep. And in IBS, it is their bowels that are in spasm. I order some basic tests to make sure that we rule out other, more serious, causes of headaches, abdominal pain, and joint pain. But by taking a good history and by performing a problem-focused exam, I have a very good idea of what the diagnosis is before I leave the exam room.

The paradigm for treating people with anxiety and depression is the same as for physical illnesses. It all starts with taking a good history. Frequently, the primary care physician, psychotherapist, or psychiatrist will treat the symptoms of anxiety or depression without fully exploring the past history of the symptoms. Many times, the source of emotional distress is situational and well-defined, for example, a difficult boss, the loss of a relationship, or an illness in the family. In the case of situational anxiety and depression, it is appropriate to proceed with treatment, such as medication and psychotherapy.

Many times, there is no situation that is proportional to the emotional distress that the patient is experiencing. Everything is stable. Why am I anxious or depressed? It could be that anxiety and depression run in the family. While the predisposition to depression and anxiety certainly has a genetic element, there is frequently a life-stressing trigger that is causing the symptoms of anxiety and depression to develop. It is still necessary to explore the fundamental cause of anxiety or depression, even if it runs in the family. We must not assume that DNA is to blame for a patient's emotional pain. Whenever the emotional pain is out of proportion to any situation that might cause the symptoms of anxiety or depression, we professionals should explore the root cause of the patient's emotional distress, instead of reflexively treating the symptoms.

PTSD and ADD

In many cases of non-situational anxiety and depression, the underlying cause is undiagnosed PTSD or ADD—even if anxiety and depression run in the family. Milder forms of PTSD and ADD are pervasive and are frequently missed by both patients and professionals because the person is high functioning. They have a good job, a spouse, children, a mortgage, and they appear and act 'normal'. But if they are in a doctor's or therapist's office to talk about their symptoms of anxiety or depression, we must consider the possibility of PTSD and ADD as the reason for their emotional distress.

We must take a good history of the patient's mental health and life experiences. Their childhood, adolescence, and young adulthood are potential sources of negative patterns of thinking and feeling that must be explored. If medical professionals do not make the correct diagnosis, we cannot prescribe the appropriate treatment. If we treat the symptoms of anxiety and depression but fail to recognize the underlying PTSD or ADD, any improvement is likely to be temporary and incomplete.

By and large, physicians and psychotherapists don't recognize how much thoughts effect emotions. Negative thoughts, especially subconscious ones, create negative emotions. It is not specific negative thoughts, but rather a pattern of negative thinking that causes anxiety and depression in PTSD and ADD. If you are always scanning for danger, always looking over your shoulder, always waiting for something bad to happen, you will likely become chronically anxious and ultimately depressed. That is what it is like for someone who has PTSD.

With ADD, you know that just getting through each day will take extraordinary amounts of time and effort. You become anxious just thinking about your daily tasks or daily work. This negative pattern of thinking about trying to finish today's work, thinking about the work from yesterday that is unfinished, and worrying about how you are going to be able to do tomorrow's work creates extreme anxiety and eventually depression. This is what it is like for someone whose ADD is affecting their ability to perform at school, at work, and even at home.

These negative patterns of thinking cause negative patterns of feelings, i.e., anxiety and depression. The patterns are not just psychological, they are neurological pathways that the brain created in such a way that different parts of the brain, with different functions, communicate with each other in real time. The thoughts and feelings have been travelling back and forth over the neuronal pathways countless times over years, or even decades, so that the responses are reflexive, automatic, and subconscious. PTSD and ADD, anxiety and depression, are neurological in structure and function, anatomically and physiologically—they are not just psychological.

We need to recognize, understand, and treat the thought processes that create anxiety and depression. Cognitive Behavioral Therapy (CBT) is a good start. The focus is on using the rational brain to reframe an emotionally painful situation. In other words, the emotions create negative thinking. If we reinterpret the event differently from a cognitive perspective, then the emotional result will be altered. While this approach is certainly valid, many medical professionals fail to recognize that the process works in reverse as well: Negative thinking creates negative emotions. Sometimes we need to use medicine to reduce the pattern of negative thinking in order to control the anxiety and depression. If we simply try to treat the emotions of anxiety and depression, we will fail to reduce the thought pattern that underlies these symptoms. We must approach the mind and the brain as a whole, each part integrated and connected. We must identify the subconscious thought patterns beneath the emotions in order to help our patients conceptualize how their minds work, as an essential part of the treatment process.

The Physical Science Behind Your Thoughts and Feelings

Neurology and psychiatry are two fields of medicine that are inadequately understood, and therefore, imperfectly treated. Of course, it's not possible to study the brain directly in living human beings. We cannot sample brain tissue and measure the levels of chemicals in the brain.

We cannot do brain biopsies of normal, healthy brains. We cannot map neuronal pathways by removing the skull and putting electrodes in the brain. Our knowledge comes from animal studies, autopsies, and measurements of brain function. Nonetheless, we have a good scientific knowledge of the basics of neuroscience.

Let's start with the anatomy, or structure, of the brain and how it relates to our thoughts and feelings. It used to be said that we only use one tenth of our brains. This is because the gray matter, the cerebral cortex or outermost part of the brain (the ten percent), is where our thoughts and action originate. In actuality, we use our entire brains. The white matter underneath the cortex is much larger, but it is not silent. It is the area where there are connections between the different parts of the brain. This is how one area of the brain communicates with other areas of the brain.

At the center of the brain is the limbic system, the emotional center of the brain. It is the structural center, but more importantly, almost all connections in the brain must pass through it. This is where physical movement is coordinated, and thoughts are connected to emotions. Furthermore, the limbic system sits on top of the hypothalamus and the pituitary gland, which is the source of hormone production (think adrenaline, cortisol, growth hormones, etc.). If we have a negative thought, it is transmitted to the limbic system where an emotion is generated, or a memory is retrieved. The pituitary gland is activated to create adrenaline and other hormones. The result is that our heart rate, blood pressure, and respiratory rate increase. While I am oversimplifying the basic science, I want to emphasize the interconnectivity of our thoughts, feelings, and physical reactions.

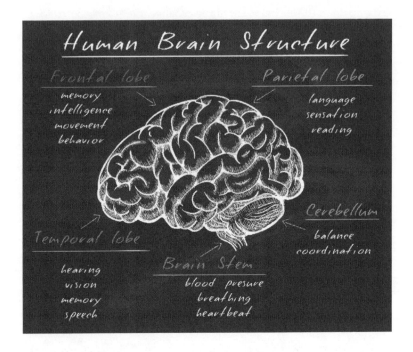

Human Brain Structure

Frontal lobe
memory
intelligence
movement
behavior

Parietal lobe
language
sensation
reading

Cerebellum
balance
coordination

Temporal lobe
hearing
vision
memory
speech

Brain Stem
blood presure
breathing
heartbeat

Thoughts and movement originate from the frontal lobe.
Specifically, thoughts are generated by the prefrontal cortex.
Executive functions such as judgement, decision-making, and
problem-solving occur here, as well. The remainder of the frontal
cortex is where we initiate muscle movement. Directly behind the
frontal cortex is the temporal lobe of the brain. The temporal lobe
is where memories are stored. It is also where speech is formed,
as well as where music and art originate. Below the temporal lobe
is the parietal lobe. Its role is to recognize patterns and interpret
sensory input, including math, language, and spatial relations.
The occipital lobe is where we sense and store visual images. Our
eyes merely transmit the images to the brain; it is the brain that

actually 'sees'. Finally, there is the cerebellum, which helps to coordinate our movements and balance.

Underneath the cortex is the white matter, the neurons that transmit information to and from different areas of the brain that allow all of the parts of the brain to communicate with each other. The limbic system, the emotional center of the brain, includes the amygdala and the hippocampus. There is a direct connection between the prefrontal cortex and the amygdala, i.e., thoughts and feelings. Finally, at the base of the brain, under the cerebellum, is the brain stem— the oldest part of the brain. It is the home of the autonomic nervous system (ANS), which is responsible for controlling all of our insensible bodily functions: respiration, body temperature, blood pressure, pulse, and peristalsis (coordination of muscle contractions in the digestive tract).

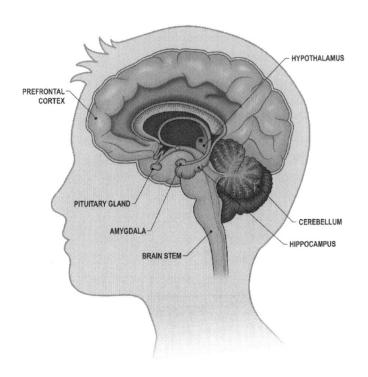

Now let's turn to the physiology, or function, of the brain and how it relates to our thoughts and feelings. You have probably heard of neurotransmitters. These are the chemicals released by the neurons, or the nerves of the brain. It is how information is transmitted from one brain cell to another brain cell.

The major neurotransmitters include dopamine, serotonin, catecholamines (norepinephrine, a generator of adrenaline), and GABA. It has been taught that anxiety and depression are caused by brain chemistry that is out of balance. For instance, the serotonin levels are too low in depression, and SSRI medications raise the levels of serotonin to treat the depression. In anxiety, the levels of catecholamine are too high.

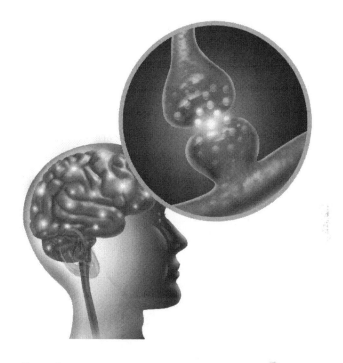

Benzodiazepines such as Ativan, Xanax, and Valium work by raising the neurotransmitter GABA, which inhibits the release of norepinephrine. However, if psychiatry were that simple, the treatment of anxiety and depression with medications would be much more successful, and I wouldn't be writing this book!

Medications are an important tool for the treatment of anxiety and depression. However, studies have consistently shown that medication and psychotherapy together work far better than either treatment by itself. Professionals in mental health have overestimated the benefits of medication and underestimated the value of psychotherapy. Many, if not most, psychiatrists practicing today only monitor their patients' medicines; they do not practice psychotherapy. While one could argue that this is a function of specialization, I believe this is due to the lack of appreciation of the value of psychotherapy by the profession.

Altering Brain Functions with Psychotherapy

Why is psychotherapy so important in the treatment of anxiety and depression? Neuroplasticity. Anxiety and depression, ADD and PTSD, are neurologic conditions as well as psychologic conditions. New technology, such as functional MRIs, are altering our understanding of how the brain works. This technique measures the blood flow to different areas of the brain during different emotional and intellectual activities. We can literally see how the brain functions in an individual, and how it differs between individuals. We can actually see how the ADD brain works differently than the non-ADD brain, and how the autistic brain works differently than the non-autistic brain. Most importantly, we can demonstrate that our brains are constantly changing—structurally and chemically. Unlike our physical bodies, which stop growing and developing after adolescence, our brains create new connections and adapt over time by remapping neuronal pathways.

For example, when someone has a stroke and a part of the brain is damaged, many times the healthy adjacent brain is able to assume the function of the injured brain—a function that it never performed previously. Similarly, the emotional connections that have been made in childhood can be remapped in adulthood. These connections are real and hardwired in the neurons and neurotransmitters in the brain. Because of neuroplasticity, we can rewire and retrain the brain to work differently. Psychotherapy is the means with which we can alter the current connections between thoughts and feelings, thus creating new and different connections. We can weaken existing connections and strengthen desirable connections. Medication alone can never do this.

In conclusion, psychology is based on neurology. The anatomy and physiology of the brain are important factors in understanding how thoughts and feelings interact, and how physical symptoms and illnesses are generated from emotions. The largest part of the brain is the white matter, the connections between the different lobes with different functions. Most importantly, all of the areas and the functions of the brain are interconnected. The neuronal pathways create patterns of integrated connections that link thoughts and feelings automatically and subconsciously. The rational, conscious, thought-producing area of the brain is one of the smallest parts, and it is mostly engaged only when one is focused on a task. The brain is more than the sum of its parts, and it is more complex than the best man-made supercomputer. The good news is that because of neuroplasticity, we can weaken the existing connections that cause anxiety and depression and create new pathways that improve our mental health. Help is on the way!

Chapter 3: What is PTSD?

What is Post Traumatic Stress Disorder? PTSD is the brain's reaction to an emotionally traumatic experience that usually occurs in childhood, adolescence, or young adulthood. It may be caused by a single catastrophic event, such as the death of a parent, or by frequent exposure to a hostile environment, such a being bullied at school. In both cases, feelings of anxiety, fear, and helplessness are generated. These feelings are reinforced on a regular basis by thinking about the past and worrying about the future, or by having to return to the toxic environment almost daily. Neurological connections are formed in the brain between thoughts, feelings, and memories. These connections become 'hardwired', subconscious, and automatic.

When the person is focused on a task and their rational brain is fully engaged, the feelings created by PTSD are suppressed. However, when the mind is allowed to wander, it returns to the subconscious thoughts and feelings created by the earlier emotional trauma. The result is anxiety and fear that seem to come from nowhere. This anxiety is not situational or logical, it is an irrational feeling of doom that can create a 'panic attack' in the short term, and depression in the longer term. Frequently, the symptoms of PTSD don't arise until later in a person's life when they think that their previous emotional trauma is resolved and scarred over.

A Life-Changing Event as the Cause of PTSD

Sometimes, a single life-changing event occurs out of the blue, unforeseen and without warning. In other words, lightning strikes on a sunny day when life is going along as usual. The sudden death of a parent or sibling, an automobile accident in which you could have died, a tree falling on your house while you slept in the next room, and an unforeseen divorce in the eyes of a child are all good examples of life-changing traumatic events. What these situations have is common is that there is no warning. You are emotionally unprepared and, therefore, shocked. From that day forward, the life that you knew is over and a new life begins. It is a watershed moment: You can date everything that happens in your life to before or after that event. It changes your circumstances, as well as how you view the world, fundamentally and completely. In most cases of PTSD, it occurs when you are particularly vulnerable—when you are a child, adolescent, or young adult.

*****

Patty is a 36-year-old psychotherapist who came to see me for a 'check-up.' It was her first visit, and I took a history. She had been diagnosed with and treated for OCD, depression, and ADD for the past two years. Her mood was much improved on medication, but she had chronic pain in her arms and legs, which her previous physicians could not figure out. In addition, she had 'chronic sinusitis' causing frequent headaches.

On exam, she appeared healthy. Her affect was appropriate, and her mood was upbeat. I found nothing abnormal during her physical exam except for tenderness of her TMJ joints (where the jaw meets the skull in front of the ears). I told her that I would draw some bloodwork to rule out a serious condition causing her

35

joint pain, but that I suspected that she had fibromyalgia and TMJ syndrome.

I explained that fibromyalgia is a condition caused by clenching the body's muscles during sleep, and that TMJ syndrome is caused by clenching the teeth and jaw muscles during sleep. Imagine clenching your hands on and off all night long—they would be painful the next day. That is what is causing your body aches. Furthermore, you do not have chronic sinusitis. Your facial pain and headaches are from clenching your teeth and jaw, which involve your jaw and facial muscles. To my surprise, she responded, "I knew it!"
Patients who have fibromyalgia frequently have underlying PTSD. At this point she starts nodding her head 'yes' as I continue to explain, "Have you ever had any emotionally traumatic events when you were younger? No one gets to twenty-one without any emotional scars. What are yours?"

Patty tells me that she had PTSD when she was thirteen. "What happened?" Her best friend was killed. "How?" He was hit by a car. "Were you there?" No, but I lived two blocks away, and I saw the ambulances rush by. "Were you romantically involved with him"? No. "Then what happened?" I had an emotional breakdown. I went to therapy and was diagnosed with, and treated for, PTSD, and I got better. I went to college, got my master's degree, and I just got married a few years ago. I continued asking question, "Do you ever think about him?" As I said, "only every day,"

Patty said "every day. I was just at the cemetery last weekend."

*****

I explained to Patty that her form of PTSD is like lightning striking on a sunny day. You are living your normal, daily life until a catastrophic event occurs out of the blue-- unforeseen, unavoidable, and emotionally devastating. That event becomes a watershed moment where there was 'life before' and 'life after' the trauma, a dividing point from which things will never be the same.

Because Patty was so young, it affected her particularly hard. Children and adolescents are narcissistic in their world view. Everything that happens is, in part, because of something that they did, or didn't do. In other words, Patty feels guilty because she thinks that she contributed to her friend's death by something she did, or by something that she didn't do. For instance, perhaps he was on the way to see her. If she never asked him to come over, he would still be alive right now. Or, if she had gone over to his house instead, he would not have been struck by the car.

These thoughts and feelings are sometimes present during the day, but they are processed every night as she clenches her body and jaws, causing Patty's fibromyalgia and TMJ syndrome. I told Patty that she needed to forgive her thirteen-year-old self. Her friend's death was not her fault. It was okay to put down her burden and to get on with her life. She needed to go back into therapy for her PTSD in order to treat her fibromyalgia and TMJ syndrome. I told her that I thought her 'OCD, depression, and

ADD' were all symptoms of her PTSD, not three different conditions or diagnoses.

If you have fibromyalgia, like Patty, you may have PTSD. Patty thought that her PTSD was in the past because she was diagnosed and treated when she was younger. She is wrong. PTSD never goes away. It may be exacerbated, or it may remit, but it cannot be 'cured'. It remains in the subconscious waiting to be triggered by a memory, a thought, or an experience. The good news is that once PTSD has been correctly diagnosed, it can be managed—just like hypertension, diabetes, high cholesterol, and other chronic conditions.

Repeated, Frequent Danger as a Cause of PTSD

The second way that PTSD occurs is by repeated, frequent danger that is unpredictable and unavoidable, and occurs over long periods of time. Think of combat or war. Even if the danger is not physical, it takes an emotional toll—day after day. For children, home and school are their entire life. If their world at home or at school is not an emotionally safe place, it becomes a war zone. Their reaction to the repeated emotional trauma is like soldier in combat. They are in eminent danger where anything bad can happen at any time. They are constantly worried, anxious, and insecure. Think of bullying at school or an emotionally and/or physically abusive parent at home. The child has no choice but to return to the toxic environment on a daily basis, worrying about the possibility of danger all of the time. Even if nothing happens today, tomorrow is another day. He or she may return to their safe place, home or school, only to experience the same risk of confrontation the next day. The brain creates a well-worn neurologic pathway of emotion: Anxiety, fear, and helplessness. The child is in 'survival mode' and their guard is never down. They are always scanning for danger, trying to prepare themselves for any and every negative eventuality. They fail to fully protect themselves because they are not in control of their situation.

Eventually, life goes on. We finish school or move out of the house, or our tour of duty ends. However, the conscious and subconscious processes of scanning for unforeseen danger remain active. The neurological pathways created by living in 'survival mode' for long periods of time are ingrained and become permanent. We are not talking about real dangers because we know what many of them are and how to avoid them. More importantly, we are talking about perceived and existential dangers: "What if this? What if that? What if my spouse dies (there is no reason to expect that they will)? What if my child gets sick? What if I lose my job (there is no logical reason to think so)? What if there is nuclear war? What if the Internet goes down and all the computers are wiped out?" I am exhausted about thinking about the endless possibilities of catastrophe that could happen at any time on any given day!

*****

Victor is a forty-nine-year-old nurse. who has been my patient for ten years. Over the past few years, he has come to me with situational anxiety. We have tried different medications, but none have helped him. When he takes medication, he feels numb but still anxious. At this visit, he tells me that his anxiety is at its worst level ever. Sure, there are stressors, but he is getting anxious even at the thought of going out for dinner with friends this coming weekend. He is always angry and irritable. His relationship with his wife and son has deteriorated because of his disagreeable and negative mood. He works overtime so that he doesn't have to be at home, yet he is unhappy at work as well. He has no enjoyment of anything in his life, and still, he knows that he has a good life and a good family. "What's wrong with me?"

We begin to explore Victor's childhood memories. I tell him that no one gets to twenty-one without some scars from childhood. What are his emotional scars? Without hesitation, he tells me that he remembers being nine years old and his father giving him money to go to the store across town, saying, "If you lose this money, don't bother coming home." Victor had to go alone and take two different buses to get there, and two different ones to return. He didn't lose the money. I said to Victor that his father seemed a little harsh: Was he? "Well, I remember him beating me with a belt several times." How did he treat your mother? "My mom took us and moved away when I was thirteen. I rarely saw my dad after that."

Victor, I said, you grew up in a war zone! Victor, you have PTSD. When you entered your house after school, you did not know what you were walking into. It was a physically and emotionally dangerous place. Your father's verbal and physical abuse to your mother, yourself, and your siblings could occur at any time and for no reason at all. You tried to protect yourself at all times. You are still trying to protect yourself now. You are always scanning for danger, waiting for something bad to happen. All of this negative thinking— conscious and unconscious—is exhausting and causes perpetual anxiety and depression.

*****

Victor may be forty-nine-years old intellectually, but he is nine years old emotionally. He can't let his guard down, even for a minute. He can't trust, smile, or let himself have fun. Victor must try to protect himself and his family at all times. And when life does not go according to plan, he doubles down and tries even harder to control his world. Even the small things, and they are all small things for Victor, reinforce his negative thoughts and feelings. He is rigid and inflexible. Victor cannot adapt and 'go with the flow'.

Since the emotional trauma occurred when he was nine, he was narcissistic in his thinking as all children are. Victor mistakenly thought and felt that everything that happened around him occurred because of something he did or didn't do. "I must have done something to make Dad angry at me." "I should have done something to protect my mom and brothers and sisters." He blames himself for not being able to prevent harm from coming to his family. And he still does. We have to have forty-nine-year-old Victor help nine-year-old Victor understand that he did the best he could in a very difficult situation. He should comfort and praise nine-year old Victor for becoming a nurse, a husband, and a father, in spite of a difficult and challenging childhood. He needs to reframe both his prior life situation and his current one to see that we only have so much control, and that not everything is

41

his fault. Victor is improved, but he is still struggling with his
PTSD today.

Bipolar Depression?

No, it's PTSD. About ten years ago, Bipolar Depression (BPD)
became the new fad diagnosis among psychiatrists. Anyone who
was happy and sad, or quiet and angry, in the same day had BPD.
If you were just plain irritable or moody, you could have BPD. If
your depression didn't respond to appropriate doses of selective
serotonin reuptake inhibitors (SSRIs), you likely had Bipolar
Depression. Psychiatrists began prescribing mood stabilizers and
second-generation antipsychotic medication, in addition to the
SSRIs. I have no idea how this fad came about, but it spread like
wildfire. And of course, the treatment failed most of the time.
Why? Because the diagnosis was wrong.

Bipolar depression is uncommon. Mania is uncommon. Most of
these patients had undiagnosed PTSD. We now understand that
the anxiety and depression that come with PTSD cause mood
swings, panic attacks, uncontrollable crying, anger, and
frustration. For those of you who have been diagnosed with BPD,
it might be worth getting reevaluated to see if you have PTSD.

*****

I have a patient, Cole, who came to me with a diagnosis
of Bipolar Depression that was made when he was
twenty years old. He was hospitalized for his mental
illness. When I met him, he was thirty-two. I asked him
to explain to me what was happening when he was
hospitalized and diagnosed with BPD. He told me that

42

he was acting out at school, depressed at home, and one day broke down and sobbed in class for forty-five minutes. When I asked him about any emotional scars that he might have suffered when he was younger, he did not hesitate to tell me that his best friend committed suicide by hanging himself the year before, when Cole was nineteen.

*****

Bipolar Depression? I don't think so, yet he still carries the diagnosis. I assured him that he did not have it. Fortunately for Cole, he has an excellent psychotherapist who helps him understand and process his emotional trauma. He no longer has mood swings and takes a small dose of an antidepressant to control his anxiety and depression.

Worrying

Without PTSD, we have perspective. Everything in life has risks. The risks of serious future events are relatively minor, and we are able to dismiss them until the time comes. When you have PTSD, the perceived risk is greatly disproportional to the actual risk. Consequently, your world view is biased and focused on the negative. You are defensive, and you let fear guide your decision-making process. Still, you succeed in making a life for yourself. You go to college, get a decent job, get married, buy a house, and have a family. Because you are focused and living life 'in the present', the emotions of PTSD are kept at bay. You are not thinking about the past and worrying about the future on a daily basis—you don't have time!

When life slows down and stabilizes, the feelings of anxiety and depression start to emerge for no apparent reason. Everything is going well. "Why do I worry so much and about every little thing? Why am I irritable and angry so much of the time? Why do I overreact to little problems or disappointments? Why can't I ever let myself be happy? I think I am depressed." You are depressed, but it's because of your undiagnosed PTSD.

More Stories

Two of my male patients, both in their thirties, had undiagnosed PTSD until we figured it out. When they were in early adolescence, fourteen and sixteen respectively, each of their fathers got sick and died. And on their deathbeds, both fathers said the same thing to their sons, "You are the man of the house now. It is up to you to take care of the family." What fourteen or sixteen-year-old boy is a man, or can function as an adult? Virtually none. I am sure that these dying men meant to encourage their boys, and that they did not think of the negative effects that their words would have on their sons.

These boys took their fathers' words to heart and literally tried to protect their mothers and siblings from the hardships caused by their deaths. Of course, they could not. Teenagers narcissistically think that most things that happen are a result of something they did or didn't do. If something unpleasant happened, it was their fault. They should have known better or should have seen it coming. They lived in constant fear and anxiety about what could happen, and then with regret and guilt when something did happen. Do you think that went away when they left their families to go to work or college? It did not. The anxiety was suppressed because they were both so busy with school and careers and families of their own. Now in their thirties, each came to me for help with their anxiety and depression.

*****

My first patient, Larry, was a functioning alcoholic. I found this out from his wife. He knew that he was depressed and that he was drinking too much, but he had a good job, a mortgage that he paid every month, and a lovely wife and daughter. His mood was depressed when I saw him, but he seemed like a 'normal' guy. Larry was self-medicating and numbing his PTSD with alcohol.

I asked Larry to tell me about his childhood. He told me about his father's death when he was a teenager, and how his dad told him that he was now the 'man of the house'. I reframed the story by helping him to see thirteen-year-old Larry from thirty-three-year-old Larry's perspective. It was unreasonable for his dad, or anyone, to expect that a thirteen-year-old boy could act like a man or a father to the rest of the family. Once he heard it and saw it from this vantage point, he understood intellectually that his feelings, self-esteem, and depression were due to unrealistic expectations that had been put upon him at the time of his father's death. I told him that he should be proud of himself for creating a successful life in spite of all of his challenges. He stopped drinking, takes antidepressants, and sees a therapist now. He is trying to allow himself to be happy.

The other man, Steve, is very successful in business and has a wonderful family. He is a hypochondriac. He is in my office at least twice per month, convinced that he has a terminal illness or is just on the edge of a heart attack. Despite normal test upon test, no amount of reassurance can comfort him for long. He is sure that unforeseen danger is just around the corner. It is a result of his PTSD from trying to be the 'man of the house' when his father died. Unfortunately, when I pointed this out to him, Steve disagreed with me. He believes that there is something physically wrong with him and chose to see another doctor.

*****

The Lasting Effect of Childhood Emotional Traumas

We all have emotional traumas in childhood and throughout our lives, but when we are young, we are particularly vulnerable because our minds are still developing. We see the world differently than we do as adults. Children and young adults think that everything that happens around them is because of something they did or didn't do and is, therefore, at least partially their fault. They feel responsible and guilty for the traumatic event. If parents are unaware or unable to recognize and mitigate emotional harm to their child, that child may develop a deep emotional wound.

On the other hand, positive life circumstances, such as close personal and family relationships, may reduce the impact of the emotional trauma. This is why some people develop PTSD and most others don't. For instance, I have a patient, Kristy, who had a difficult childhood because her parents were so strict and punished their children severely. However, she had three sisters, and they all supported each other. Kristy does not have PTSD. She has nothing more than the situational anxieties and occasional depressed mood that all people experience. All of us have emotional scars from our childhood. People who have PTSD have unresolved emotional wounds that have not been scarred over.

Both the event itself and the age (stage) in life when the event occurs will determine the severity of the PTSD. If there are strong positive influences in the person's life when the emotionally traumatic event occurs, PTSD may not develop at all. The more vulnerable a person is, the greater impact the traumatic event will have on their emotional well-being at the time, and in the future. Remember, the signs and symptoms of PTSD may not arise until later in life, when circumstances become stable and we are not consumed by daily life—completing school or climbing the occupational ladder. When there is time to allow the mind to think about the distant past and think about the unforeseeable future, we are the most vulnerable to our previous emotional traumas.

Awareness

If you feel anxious or depressed without a situational cause, you might have PTSD. To find out, pay attention to where your mind goes when you allow it to wander: When you are driving, in the shower, or watching a movie that is not very interesting to you. What do you think about? What do you worry about? Everyone has emotional scars from their childhood. What are yours? You probably think that you have gotten over your traumas, but the truth is that you have suppressed them as life moved on, and the practicalities of making a life took precedence. Now, your life is more stable—you are out of school, your career path is determined, and your children are in school and don't need as much attention.

Your conscious, rational brain is less engaged. There is room for the subconscious emotional brain to rise to the level of consciousness. Your anxiety is just below the surface. It is a feeling, not a thought. You are anxious and depressed, but you can't understand why. The emotional traumas of childhood are not scars. Rather they are open, festering wounds coming to the surface and begging to be lanced. How were you affected by your parents' divorce? Were you bullied at school? Did you have ADD and you underachieved? Was there a death in the family that changed your life when it occurred? Was your father or mother physically or verbally abusive? Did you have a near-death experience, such as a car accident? Did you have a serious illness requiring months or years of medical treatment?

The source of your PTSD is a cataclysmic event, or an omnipresent danger that occurred when you were younger, that is causing your anxiety and depression today. How can that be? That was so long ago. And whatever happened is in the past and is no longer happening. "I've moved on, gotten over it, and put it behind me." That is rational, but we are dealing with emotions which are irrational. While your rational brain aged chronologically, your emotional brain is stuck at the time of your trauma.

I frequently point out to my patients who have PTSD that there are two people inside your brain: An older you, the forty-year-old person that you are today, and a younger you, the ten-year-old person that you were then. The source of your PTSD is that the ten-year-old has been silenced, despised, and repressed for so long. He is still ten years old emotionally. He needs to grow up and become an adult in an emotional sense.

When the forty-year-old is visited by the feelings of the ten-year-old, he reverts back to those emotions of helplessness, fear, insecurity, and loneliness. The forty-year-old worries, irrationally, that something unforeseen and catastrophic is going to happen— in essence, lightning will strike and destroy everything he has. Even though this defies logic, he can't help thinking negatively. This pattern of negativity is automatic and pervasive. It is easy to see how this constant worrying and being on guard is exhausting, anxiety-provoking, and ultimately depressing. Imagine viewing the world as an unfriendly, dangerous, and unpredictable place in which we must constantly scan for danger. We must protect ourselves and our loved ones at all times from any and all threats, no matter how unlikely. Generalized anxiety and chronic depression is often the result.

How do you start to resolve your anxiety, your depression, your PTSD? First and foremost, by acknowledging that you have it. You have avoided your ten-year-old self for as long as you can remember. You despise him for being the weakling that he is, for everything he did to survive, and for everything he didn't do to change his situation. Stop. Look around. As a forty-year-old, ask yourself, "What ten-year-old child could do anything differently or better than I did?" It was a struggle just to survive, day to day.

You must embrace the ten-year-old self instead of ignoring him. You must try to be empathetic, not judgmental; loving, not disdainful; and nurturing, not dismissive. In short, the forty-year-old you must parent the ten-year-old. That's correct. The Adult, rational you must accept and embrace the emotional Child and become the parent of that Child. You must treat that Child as you would treat any ten-year-old child—with understanding, empathy, love, and compassion. You must help the Child understand that whatever happened was not their fault. They did the best they could in the given circumstances. You must praise the ten-year-old for having survived and for becoming successful in spite of the challenges and adversity he or she faced. You must help the Child mature emotionally. The Adult must help the Child learn to trust again—other people, life, and themselves.

Learning is a process, and it will take six months to two years of daily parenting to alter the patterns of thinking and feeling. The brain must create new connections between thoughts and emotions. The process must be repeated and practiced regularly to strengthen the connections. It is not just the passage of time, but rather an active, daily, conscious exercise of parent-child interaction that will result in the enhancement of your EQ (Emotional Quotient), so that it more closely matches your IQ. When that happens, you will feel less anxious and more secure because you will both know and feel that you can take care of yourself and can handle life's challenges— rationally and emotionally. It takes time and effort. Be patient.

One last observation: PTSD does not go away, just as the death of a loved one doesn't go away. There will be circumstances that will trigger emotional memories, and your mind will automatically go back to that dark place of fear, despair, and helplessness. Expect it. When that happens, you emotionally revert back to the Child. As the Adult, use the same techniques that you used before to calm, soothe, and reassure the Child that they are reacting (overreacting) to this situation. The feelings are perfectly normal and understandable, but they are out of proportion to the problem at hand. Together, as both Adult and Child, you will work them out. Trust each other. Be brave. Be logical and smart. Make the best decisions you can with the information that you have, and then let the situation play out. No matter what happens, you will survive and then go on from there, knowing that you did the best you could in a situation that was beyond your control. When the drama plays out, give both your Adult and Child credit. Success breeds success. With each successful resolution of conflicts, the emotional trauma of the PTSD will lose power and your ability to trust yourself and your life will grow.

Chapter 4: How Do I Get Help for My PTSD?

When you have PTSD, there are two parts of your brain competing for attention and control—the adult that you are now, and the younger self that you were when your emotional trauma occurred. Your present self is rational, and it thinks. Your former self is emotional, and it feels. For those who do not have PTSD, their rational brain is in control of their emotional brain. Their anxiety is mostly situational and appropriate. With PTSD, the emotional self is in control of the rational brain. Worrying is generalized and hypothetical, and you worry about everything and nothing at all with equal intensity. I call this 'existential' worrying. It is endless and out of proportion to the situation. It causes anxiety, fear, and helplessness—the same emotions you felt at the time of the emotional trauma. You think that you have put your past behind you and that you have scars, as we all do. You are wrong. You have an open wound that has never healed, and your PTSD from your past is creating your worrying and anxiety today.

The Adult and The Child

People who are suffering from PTSD have a disconnect between their IQ and the EQ— between their rational intelligence and their emotional intelligence. Your IQ is your rational and intellectual brain and represents your true age. Your EQ is your emotional brain, and it is stuck at the age that you first experienced the trauma causing your PTSD—most likely in your childhood. With PTSD, there is a disconnect between the intellectual, rational 'Adult' you, and the emotional, irrational 'Child' you. The Adult resides in the cognitive, thoughtful part of

52

the brain. The Child resides in the subconscious, emotional brain. Furthermore, there is little or no communication between your Adult brain and your Child brain. The Adult despises the Child and tries to avoid or suppress him or her at all times and at all costs. The Child, however, will not be denied. He or she demands attention and will always be just below the surface. The Child makes their thoughts and feelings known whenever the Adult is not focusing on something objective, such as work, activities, or sports. When the rational mind is not engaged, the Child is in control. To understand what I mean, pay attention to your mind when you allow it to wander—when you are in the shower, driving, or not paying attention to the movie you are watching. What are you thinking about? How does that make you feel? Whatever your answer, that is what is bothering you. The Child is trying to get your attention. In order to understand and to resolve your PTSD, you need the Adult and the Child to start communicating with each other.

How can you get the Adult and the Child to communicate? Purposefully. Your Adult must acknowledge your Child, instead of trying to ignore him or her. Furthermore, the Adult must listen to, embrace, nurture, accept, love, and forgive the Child for everything that the Child has done, or has failed to do, in the past. The Child is stuck at the age when the event(s) that caused the PTSD occurred. However, the Adult judges the Child as if he or she had the knowledge and experience of the Adult at that time. The Adult thinks, "He should have…; he could have…; she shouldn't have…." The Adult blames the Child, and the Child believes that it is their fault.

As the Adult, you need to look around you. What school-age child can successfully defend themselves from a bully? How can any child do anything but survive in the face of emotional, physical, or sexual abuse? The Adult must empathize with the Child and forgive him or her, not judge and castigate the Child. Then, the Adult and the Child must communicate with each other. Literally. Verbally. Frequently. Honestly. The Adult must try to understand the Child instead of silencing him or her. Once the Adult understands the Child's message, a conversation should then ensue between them. Literally. In doing so, the Adult will help the Child to understand and mature, so that he or she becomes more rational and less emotional—to grow up and be less fearful and anxious. The goal is to diffuse the power of those negative connections and emotional memories so that we can focus on our present lives, instead of thinking about the past and worrying about the future.

Psychotherapy

If you think that you have PTSD, you probably do. The first thing to do is to start a journal and write about your feelings. Let the thoughts and emotions flow freely without editing or interpretation. You are not writing a story or keeping a diary. Use this journal as often as you want or need to, whenever you feel compelled to do so. Then, look for a professional with whom you feel comfortable. It may be your family physician or the psychologist that you have been seeing or have seen in the past. If your primary care physician does not have the time or ability to discuss the underlying reasons for your anxiety or depression, ask for a referral to a psychologist. Your physician will likely prescribe medications which will help with your symptoms, but you still need psychotherapy to understand where your symptoms are coming from, and how your past history relates to your present anxiety and depression.

Finding the right therapist can be challenging. You must feel a personal connection so that you can trust the professional to guide you. If you don't feel a connection 'in your gut' after two or three sessions, move on to another psychotherapist. Different therapists have distinct personalities and styles that match some patients, but not others. It's not personal—you won't hurt their feelings. Bad therapy can be worse than no therapy, so find a therapist who resonates with you. You should 'click'. You might have to try a few professionals before you feel comfortable trusting one with your emotional well-being.

In addition to individual psychotherapy, group psychotherapy is an effective way to treat people with PTSD. Most importantly, you realize that you are not alone. Everyone there has a PTSD story and suffers from the symptoms of anxiety and depression. The response that you get from the group is likely to be empathetic and nurturing. In sharing your story, you must communicate with yourself before you can communicate with others. When you hear other stories, they validate your feelings. Shared stories reduce the power of our negative emotions.

The Role of Medication with Psychotherapy

Medications are very useful and effective as part of your treatment. Studies have shown that medication and psychotherapy work much better together than either one by itself. The medications help to control the anxiety and the obsessive negative thinking so that you are receptive to the cognitive therapy. The goal is to reestablish the dominance of the rational brain over the emotional brain. When the EQ controls the IQ, the Child is making the decisions. The Adult must be rational and must put the situation into perspective as objectively as possible. The Adult may say, "Yes, things didn't work out, but it was not my fault and I did the best I could do in the circumstances." If the Child is in control, they may blame themselves. Medications help you put one foot in front of the other to keep working towards your goal.

A common misconception about medications is that they make you feel like someone else. Nothing could be further from the truth. Medications allow you to be who you really are. This anxious, depressed person is not the real you. In addition, there is no 'happy' pill. Being 'happy' all of the time is not normal! Remember in high school how you felt when you looked at your classmates and thought, "Why is everyone so happy and I am so miserable?" As an adult now, you realize that everyone else was miserable, too, and that they were looking at you and thinking the same thing, "Why is he or she so happy when I am so miserable?" It can seem that way when we adults are anxious or depressed.

Many of you have been on medications that have not worked. If you were treating the symptoms instead of the cause of your anxiety and depression, medication will not work very well. Now, we need to make the correct diagnosis by defining the cause of your anxiety and depression, whether it be situational, hereditary, ADD, or PTSD. Next, we need to create a recipe for success. This includes therapy, medication, and homework. Medication can be prescribed by your family doctor or by a psychiatrist.

There are three categories of medications that we use to create a cocktail to effectively reduce the anxiety, the depression, and the negative thoughts. The most recent development in medications focuses on the negative thought process. When the antianxiety and antidepressant medications are not working, many physicians now add second generation (atypical) antipsychotic medications. Whoa! Did you just say 'psychotic'? Yes. Psychosis is primarily a thought disorder. What we are finally coming to terms with is the fact that thoughts and feelings are inextricably linked, and constantly feed each other. For some people, their thoughts primarily affect their feelings. In order to effectively reduce their anxiety and depression, we must turn down the negative thought process. We have found that small doses of antipsychotic medications are very effective when added to the standard antidepressant and antianxiety medications.

*****

Edith is a thirty-five-year-old patient who recently learned that she inherited the autosomal dominant gene that will cause her to develop the same chronic disease as one of her parents. Prior to taking this genetic testing, she suffered from extreme anxiety for fear that she might have the gene. Now that she knows for sure that she does have it, she is naturally depressed. It is the negative thoughts—not her anxiety—that keep her from responding to antidepressant medications. By adding a medicine that dials down the thought process, we have helped her stay in the present so that she can focus on her life now instead of constantly worrying about her life ten to fifteen years from now.

*****

Homework

I tell my patients to try to stay in the present so that they don't think about the past and worry about the future. Children are happy because yesterday never happened, and tomorrow will never come. As adults, we need to be more responsible, but we need to try to do so rationally rather than emotionally. Easier said than done. The key is to focus on what you are doing instead of how you are doing. The brain is constantly working. If we don't give it something objective and outside of ourselves to think about, such as work, a hobby, or a sport, the brain will look inward—and that is not good for any one of us. When we start to remember the past, worry about the future, and judge ourselves by unfair and unrealistic standards, anxiety and depression are frequently the result. Get busy. Play golf, tennis, or bridge. Join a book club, a church group, or a bowling league. Volunteer or take a part-time job, regardless of the pay. Take an art or music class or audit a course at a local community college or university. It is important for all of us to have a reason to get out of bed, a place to go, and adult relationships.

We need to make new friends when we feel alone and lonely. Not every new friend has to be a 'best' friend. There can be friends with whom you share coffee, moving-going friends, and bowling or golf friends. You want to nurture these new friendships by extending them to include phone calls, dinners together, and other shared interests. In doing so, you will create a network of friends and support so that there are multiple people with whom to engage when you feel alone, lonely, or depressed. Through those activities and friends, you will meet other people who you would not have met otherwise, and they may become your new friends, as well. It's like starting an exercise program. You make every excuse in the world to avoid going to the gym, but when you get there, you actually enjoy yourself until the next time when you have to force yourself to go because you 'don't feel like it'. Go anyway. This is the work. It takes effort and practice until it comes naturally, and you look forward to your new activities and friends.

<u>Try It Again</u>

For those of you who have tried medication and or psychotherapy in the past, I would ask you to consider trying it again. The chances for successful treatment have changed due to circumstances. First, you are in a different place in your life. Your life experience and your intellectual understanding of the facts of life are probably much more advanced than they were in the past. Second, our professional understanding of how the mind works has also advanced. There are very few therapists today who practice psychoanalysis, the technique described and used by Dr. Sigmund Freud. Most psychotherapists use a form of behavioral cognitive therapy that is much more interactive between the patient and the therapist. This therapy is more of a dialogue instead of a monologue. The focus is on understanding the facts, and then helping you see the situation differently than you had before. This is called 'reframing' the event, allowing you to see the circumstances of your trauma from a different, more rational and objective perspective instead of an emotional perspective. The facts are the same, but the interpretation and understanding are different. Third, our understanding and use of medication has matured. Instead of trying one medication at a time, which may not have worked for you in the past, we may choose to recommend a combination of medicines that work together to address both your thoughts and your feelings.

Hopefully, I have empowered you with an insight into what might be driving your feelings of anxiety and depression—your underlying ADD or PTSD. If you find yourself identifying with my descriptions of ADD or PTSD, and you have not yet been formally diagnosed with either, now is the time to seek help. Whatever treatment you had in the past was likely ineffective because the correct diagnosis was elusive. Make an appointment with your family doctor, or with a psychotherapist, and tell them what you suspect. "I have ADD or I have PTSD." Don't wait for them to diagnose you. If you think that you have ADD or PTSD, you probably do. You can save time and money by helping your clinician verify the diagnosis so that your treatment can begin immediately.

Chapter 5: What is ADD?

Before I answer that question, let's first talk about what ADD is not. ADD is not psychological; it is neurological. ADD is not laziness; people with ADD work harder than those without it in order to achieve similar results. ADD is not volitional; no one would choose to classify themselves as having ADD just to receive medication or special treatment. ADD is not all or none; a person may have very mild to very severe ADD. ADD does not mean failure; most people with ADD are successful until they hit a wall. Some of the most successful and famous people in the world have ADD.

ADD is an inherited, hardwired, operating system of the brain that differs in many respects from the non-ADD brain. We can see that there are differences by using the newer technologies of MRIs and PET scans to track the flow of blood through the brain. Think of the two systems as an Apple vs. a PC. For decades, there has been a debate among the medical community, educators, and parents as to whether ADD is a real condition or just an excuse to justify the underachievement of some students. Are they just lazy, unmotivated, procrastinating, and not serious or interested in their schoolwork? How can so many children have ADD? If everyone has ADD, then no one has ADD. Why now? We never had this many people diagnosed and treated for ADD in the past. It must be a fad that will pass.

Because we can now scientifically see that the ADD brain functions differently than the non-ADD brain by using advanced technology and scans, we must recognize that ADD is both real and common. Studies have estimated that almost ten percent of the population has ADD. It is NOT a disease. It is NOT learned. It is genetic and inherited from a parent. Therefore, it starts from birth and NEVER goes away. It has always been present in every generation. However, until today's fast-paced, highly technical, multitasking, computer-based society evolved, having ADD did not necessarily affect one's ability to perform in school, work, or in life. When many of us were shopkeepers, truck drivers, factory workers, tradesmen, farmers, carpenters, or postal workers, we could do our jobs well in spite of having ADD. People gravitated to professions, jobs, and hobbies where their ADD was not a hindrance. In addition, for many people with ADD, it was a gift! They were more creative, more spontaneous, and they took more risks that yielded successful outcomes. They saw the bigger picture, the forest through the trees, and capitalized on making their visions a reality.

ADD and Children

Let's dispel all of the myths, suppositions, and innuendos about ADD once and for all. ADD is a normal variant of the hardwired operating system of the brain. It is not pathological—it is just different. Children and their parents, for the most part, are not aware that they have ADD unless they have a more severe case. These children are not lazy, stupid, or unmotivated. It is just more challenging for them to perform the educational tasks required in our rigid 'one size fits all' educational system. They frequently procrastinate because it is too difficult, frustrating, and painful to do what seems reasonable and natural to someone with a non-ADD brain. Some ADD children may be labeled 'oppositional-defiant' because they refuse to participate in school or situations at home where they know they are doomed to fail.

Some children have the ability to hyper-focus under pressure and therefore hide their ADD. Adrenaline and other neurotransmitters are released in response to the fear of failure or punishment, overriding their ADD brain and allowing these students to eventually get their work done. They may ultimately perform very well. However, the amount of time, effort, and anxiety expended in doing so takes a toll on the child. What do you think happens with the next assignment? The child knows how difficult it will be to complete. He or she procrastinates, becomes anxious, runs out of time, gets an extension, and eventually completes the task. Until next time... and on and on. This exacts a heavy toll on their self-esteem and confidence, which can lead to chronic anxiety and depression.

Many children with ADD will be able to play video or computer games, draw or play music, or work with their hands for hours at a time. How can they focus when performing these activities when they can't focus on their schoolwork? Does that mean that they don't have ADD? The short answer is NO. In many cases, ADD negatively affects the auditory processing function of the brain, and positively affects the visual and pattern recognition functions of the brain. The child focuses and excels at activities that are visual and avoids activities that are primarily auditory. (A more detailed explanation follows later in this chapter). It is human nature to avoid tasks that are painful and to gravitate to those that are pleasurable.

ADD and Adults

ADD affects every aspect of life, not just work or school—a messy room, dirty laundry, relationships, projects started but never completed, and unpaid bills and bounced checks. The busy brain even causes sleep deprivation by waking you up in the middle of the night. Since ADD is present at birth and continues throughout life, every experience that you have ever had must take into account the way in which your brain functions. In some cases, such as school, ADD had a negative impact. In other cases, such as music, art, and sports, ADD may have had a positive impact. However, the more severe your ADD, the more likely that the net impact on your life and daily activities has been negative. If you are reading this book and you think you have ADD, it may be the cause of your anxiety and depression.

People with ADD have a 'busy' brain. What does that mean? It means that their minds are racing, thinking multiple random thoughts simultaneously. Imagine having many different screens open on your computer, and the computer shuffling the screens without you being able to stop it. That's ADD. You can't finish reading one screen before it jumps to another screen that involves a totally different subject or thought process. You have to wait until that screen comes up in the shuffle again, by which time you may have forgotten much of what you read before. How could you possibly get anything done? I am exhausted just thinking about it! Only caffeine and adrenaline (both stimulants) will help the person with ADD focus by slowing down brain activity so that they can complete their task.

In contrast, a person who does not have ADD is able to voluntarily think about a subject for as long as he or she chooses. Then it is filed away in their memory bank and another subject is taken up. In our analogy above, we open a new window on our computer; expand it; work on it; click on links; close links; then minimize or exit the window and open a new window. We are able to focus on one task at a time and see it through to completion before starting another task. If we get distracted by something, we can put the original task aside, pay attention to the new issue, and then return to the original task where we left off.

Visual and Auditory Processing

There are challenges and benefits to the person who has ADD. But before we go there, it is important to understand something about the ADD brain that has not been adequately recognized or explored: Most people with ADD are visual thinkers. What does that mean, and why should that matter? Temple Grandin, an authority on autism, helped us to understand that human beings think primarily in one of three modalities: Words, pictures, and patterns. I would submit that we all learn in multiple ways, but for each person, there is one dominant way in which we think and learn. For instance, I am a person who thinks in words. When I retrieve a memory, I hear a story. My son, on the other hand, sees the pictures. In other words, if I think about the last family holiday we celebrated, I think about where we were, who was there, and what we had to eat. When my son does the same thing, he sees a picture. He can tell me details that I don't remember because my brain does not see the picture. Try it yourself. Think about your last birthday. Do you see a picture? Or do you hear the words when you try to remember it? How many little details can you remember such as the clothes that people wore, the writing on the cake, the color of the tablecloth?

Let's take it one step further. Temple Grandin tells us that visual thinkers make movies from their visual memories. When they retrieve a memory, they see a picture. Now, in their mind, they can turn that picture into a movie that they can rewind and fast-forward. What do I mean by fast-forward? They can imagine what will happen in the future. This is one of the reasons that people who have ADD are creative. They can take an idea (a picture) and let it play out in their mind (a movie) to reach the final product. They see the end as well as the beginning. This is likely true for pattern thinkers as well. Artists, musicians, and astrophysicists all see the whole painting, hear the melody, and conceptualize the math all on a blank canvass, music score, or white board.

Most people are primarily auditory thinkers. But imagine being a visual thinker in school. First, the classroom is a place where we hear the teacher's lecture. This is augmented by slides, graphs, and black or whiteboards that we can see. The homework consists primarily of reading (an auditory brain function). Then the testing is, you guessed it, verbal. You have to read the question and write the answer or read the question and then choose the correct answer from several multiple choices. Simple, right? Not if you are a visual thinker.

For a visual thinker, the student has to read the question, convert the words to a picture in their mind, play the movie backwards and forwards in their mind, determine the correct answer, then convert the picture in their mind to words in order to put the answer on paper or on the computer screen. Wow! As an auditory thinker, it would be akin to being taught primarily in pictures (which would be converted to words in the brain), and then tested by having to draw a picture, or pick the correct picture out of several pictures that all look the same except for one minor detail (think of the magazines where you are asked to match the correct picture or drawing to the featured one. It takes me forever!). Not only would it be challenging, but it would take more time. The grade, i.e., performance, would not be an accurate reflection of one's understanding or intelligence.

I have had this conversation with one of my patients, a professor of education at Princeton University. She agrees that there are primary verbal and primary visual learners. However, she points out to me that there are no scientific studies that show that teaching visual learners preferentially with visual modalities improves their performance. It has taken me awhile to figure out the answer to this riddle. The answer is: How do we test their knowledge? Verbally. The studies are flawed because we give the visual learners a standard auditory test to see how much they have learned! No wonder they can't perform. Visual learners are visual thinkers, and they excel at visual tasks. Many private and specialized schools such as The Friends Schools have known this for a long time. However, even they test their students primarily in the standard verbal method because the educational and business worlds favor the majority of us who are auditory thinkers.

Each one of us thinks and remembers in all three ways (words, pictures, and patterns), and the ratio is different for each of us as well. While I am primarily an auditory thinker and my son is primarily a visual thinker, my wife is about seventy-five percent auditory and twenty-five percent visual in terms of her memory function. This becomes apparent when we talk about a shared memory such as a vacation and she remembers (sees) details that I don't remember. Or when she can't remember (hear) a title or author of a book that we both read, or the name of the artist who painted a famous painting that we both like. Since auditory and visual thinking is not one or the other, but rather some of one and some of the other, it makes sense that the greater the amount the brain functions in the auditory mode, the better the performance will be on a verbal test. The greater the amount of visual brain functioning, the worse the performance will be on a verbal test. This is one of the reasons why some people with ADD will be recognized earlier than someone who is not diagnosed until college or beyond.

Challenges

The ADD brain has two major challenges: The inability to completely focus on the task at hand, and the dominant visual process of making and retrieving memories. How does this play out in the real world? How does having ADD create anxiety and, in more severe cases, depression? At some point, many people with ADD hit a wall. The more severe the ADD, the earlier they hit that wall. Children will have difficulty in school, especially completing assignments or taking tests. "He is so smart, but his grades are only fair." "She works so hard but when it comes to exam time, she can't remember anything." "I always procrastinate and wait until the last minute to get my paper in." Sound familiar?

The combination of the busy and distracted brain plus the visual method of creating and retrieving memories puts the student at a disadvantage compared to the majority of their peers. It takes longer to learn because most schoolwork is verbal. The memories created and stored by the student are likely incomplete (like the visual memories in my brain). Therefore, when the student is tested, they retrieve the memory that is incomplete. You cannot remember what you did not store. Hence, they perform poorly on tests. Now, think what happens to the student when every day, they are struggling with the same process. It's like the movie, *Groundhog Day*. It is natural and logical that most people would avoid this unpleasantness if possible. It is not possible because we are required to take tests and write papers and do math in school. The student with ADD procrastinates, or spends hour after hour studying, only to get an average or poor grade. The teacher knows that the grade does not reflect the student's intelligence, so 'extra credit' assignments may be given to improve their score. Until the next time…

When given task after task that is going to take an extraordinary amount of time and effort, only to result in a disappointing outcome, it is logical and natural that the child becomes anxious, frustrated, and oppositional. Both their behavior and their mood will reflect this. When the same child is doing something that comes more naturally and easily to him or her, such as sports, puzzles, drawing, or video games, they are happy and relaxed. It makes sense, correct? It is human nature. But the child must return to school, of course. School is an academic war zone for some of these children. Daily and chronic anxiety can lead to depression, and in some cases, PTSD. What is the definition of insanity? Doing the same thing over and over again and expecting a different result! What happens to the child's self-esteem when they continue to underperform in school? What happens when he or she is teased and criticized because of their 'stupidity' or 'laziness'? Anxiety. Depression. PTSD.

For those people with milder ADD, they might not hit that wall of frustration until high school or college. They have been able to succeed long enough that their reaction to the unexpected underperformance is primarily anxiety. "Why am I struggling? Will I be able to catch up? I haven't finished last night's assignment; how can I possibly finish today's homework?" I am anxious just thinking about it. "And I have to clean my room and do my chores." College is an especially vulnerable time for people with mild ADD because it is much less structured than primary education and requires so much more reading and self-learning. I see this in my practice frequently. It is one reason why only 60 percent of students who start college finish and only 40 percent of Americans have college degrees. Again…what is the definition of insanity?

I also see adults who struggle at work because of their mild ADD. The workplace has changed dramatically in the digital age. Many vocations, such as auto mechanics, are exceedingly technical and computer based. Many auto salesmen are required to receive training and take competency exams on the computer. Real estate agents have to complete mountains of paperwork that was never required when they were first licensed. People with ADD used to gravitate to professions that minimized the challenges of having ADD: salesperson, mechanic, carpenter, construction worker, farmer, or truck driver. However, the requirements demanded of today's employees in almost every profession can affect the performance of those who have ADD. When training is involved, either in the classroom or on the computer, the person with ADD may struggle. When exams are required for certification for careers in cosmetology, wastewater management, and early childcare, the person with ADD may struggle. When companies are sold or acquired by another company and a new system must be learned, the person with ADD may struggle.

These are some of the scenarios that I have heard from my adult patients who are unaware that they have ADD. They come to me because of anxiety, depression, or poor performance at work. "Everything was fine until...." Or, "I am very successful performing my job, but I can't pass the exams." In taking a history, I learn that their children or their siblings have ADD. I ask them how they did in school. Not surprisingly, they got by but did not do well. Because it was difficult and frustrating, they chose to focus on extracurricular activities and didn't take school too seriously. Now they are adults and are in jeopardy of losing their job, not qualifying for a promotion, or unable to start a new career because their brain cannot focus clearly on the new material that must be mastered. The time required to study is prohibitive, and the ability to retain new information is impaired, resulting in poor performance on standardized testing.

They need medication to treat their ADD now as an adult, even though they never did as a child. I prescribe medication to be used as a tool to help them focus and perform in the areas in which they struggle because they have ADD. These adults don't need medication every day or for extended periods of time. They have learned to live their lives and do their jobs by using compensatory strategies, and by gravitating to jobs and activities that they perform well. The reason that it seems that 'everyone' has ADD is because the world has changed.

Summary

To summarize, ADD is real and neurological, affecting almost ten percent of human beings. The effects on a child's self-esteem, mood, and behavior can be devastating if ADD is not diagnosed and treated properly. ADD is lifelong and can become a problem in adulthood, even if it was well compensated in childhood. ADD can lead to acute and chronic anxiety, as well as depression, in both children and adults. For anxious and depressed patients who have newly diagnosed or untreated ADD, the first line of treatment is NOT antianxiety medications or antidepressants; it is ADD medication. In addition, if their anxiety or depression does not resolve by treating their ADD, psychotherapy and additional medications may be needed as well. Remember, their life experiences have been affected by their ADD, including their self-esteem, their underachievement, and even their relationships. In addition to ADD, they may also have PTSD.

It may seem complicated, but when you start at the beginning, i.e., ADD, it is logical to comprehend how a person's ADD is causing their anxiety, depression, and PTSD now. If you think that you or one of your children may have ADD, please get tested and treated. If you are prescribed an ADD medication, it will be a life-changing, WOW experience. If not, you probably don't have ADD.

Chapter 6: How Do I Get Help for My ADD?

To answer that question, it is important to acknowledge two principles: Not all people with ADD need medication, and medication alone is not sufficient for treating symptomatic ADD. Many people have been successful in both their professional and personal lives without even knowing that they have ADD. Since it isn't broken, we don't have to fix it! In fact, those people are likely successful, in part, because of their ADD. However, for others who are struggling because of their ADD, stimulant medication is only part of the answer.

There are consequences of their living with ADD—low self-esteem, underachievement, anxiety, and depression. Medication that helps people focus allows them to perform better in the present and complete their daily tasks. This will reduce their anxiety of not being able to complete their homework or projects at work because they now know that they can finish what they start. For adults who are recently diagnosed with ADD, we need to also consider the emotional consequences of living with it until now. We must address their anxiety, depression, and PTSD as a result of living with undiagnosed and untreated ADD. Psychotherapy and antidepressant medication may be necessary.

How Many People Really Have ADD?

There is a misconception surrounding the diagnosis and treatment of ADD in both public and professional circles that ADD is over diagnosed and over treated. Nothing could be further from the truth. The statistics often quoted are that five to seven percent of children have ADD. In my experience, I think that it is likely higher. Professionals are not recognizing the milder forms of ADD that don't get diagnosed until later in life. Many people are not affected by their ADD until after high school or later. In those situations, the individual is able to compensate for their ADD by working harder and longer to achieve relative success—until they hit a wall.

In addition, there are many parents who suspect or know that their child has ADD, but resist treating them with medication. Readers, I implore you to help your children by getting them tested and treated with medication (along with other strategies). Why? There are many reasons, but the most important one is self-esteem. Many children think that they are stupid, different, and a failure because they cannot perform in school as well as children who do not have ADD. They do not understand the constructs of ADD, but they are extremely sensitive to the consequences of having it. Children and young adults may become moody and oppositional. They may engage in risky behavior such as early sexual activity, drug use, and dangerous activities. They will naturally gravitate to anything that they are good at and gives them positive reinforcement while avoiding homework and other activities that are overwhelming and unpleasant.

The result is that the child can become anxious when faced with new challenges in school because they know how much work and how much time it will take to succeed. That is the best-case scenario. Many times, the student will fall behind and not catch up. This can lead to underachievement, underemployment, and depression later in life. In fact, studies show that sixty-five percent of unmedicated children with ADD have a comorbid psychiatric condition such as anxiety, depression, learning disorders, or oppositional-defiant disorder. These children have three times the risk of going to jail and four times the risk of committing suicide as compared to the non-ADD population. Parents, if your child starts to struggle in school, avoids doing homework, or exhibits personality changes, please get them tested for ADD. If they are diagnosed with ADD, please help them by accepting medication if it is recommended.

Anxiety and Undiagnosed ADD

Most of you who are reading this book are adults. You may have ADD, or you may have a family member or loved one who has ADD. Your anxiety today is likely because you have hit a wall. You are overwhelmed, and you are starting to fall behind at work or in your personal life. You are on edge, you can't sleep, and your relationships suffer. Your depression today is because you feel that you have underachieved in life.

Here's another scenario. You are in your thirties or forties, and you feel that very real midlife crisis. Your self-esteem is poor, and you are discontented. You're depressed and are looking for an answer because you don't want to feel this way for the rest of your life. The PTSD that you have today may be from your ADD. School was a war zone for you, and you are still looking over your shoulder for the next bad thing to happen. You can't let your guard down. You rarely laugh or smile. Nothing is pleasurable. You withdraw and feel alone and lonely. I assure you, friends, there is still hope for you.

If you have anxiety because of your ADD that has been unrecognized, treating you with ADD medication will allow you to get your work done. By completing your tasks today, you will stop thinking about the work that you didn't do yesterday and stop worrying about starting new projects tomorrow. You will, once again, feel in control of your life. Your anxiety and sleep deprivation will resolve, and you will feel like yourself, not this anxious person who is not really you. You may need medication on a 'prn', or as-needed, basis only. For instance, you may only need it to help you focus in meetings, in continuing education or training sessions, or in managing complex projects. Unlike children or young adults with ADD, you don't necessarily have to take it every day. You probably won't need antianxiety medication either. Instead of treating the symptoms of anxiety, we will be treating the cause of the anxiety.

If you have depression or PTSD as a result of having untreated ADD in school, the approach to your treatment is more complex but still very effective. It may be necessary to treat the depression or PTSD first, unless the ADD is causing a problem in your daily activities. Medication for ADD might not help at this stage. Antidepressants and psychotherapy are the first step.

CBT (Cognitive Behavioral Therapy) will help you to understand the source of your depression. You will begin to recognize that what happened to you when you were in school was not your fault: You did the best you could, given the fact that you were born with a brain that worked differently. Furthermore, you did not receive the necessary help from your parents, teachers, or doctors. This is not assigning blame; it's just a fact. You need to forgive yourself for anything that you did, or didn't do, as a consequence of having ADD. You need to start a new chapter in your life, no matter how old you are.

Let's start now with this newfound knowledge to create something different and enjoyable. Start a new sport, hobby, or project that utilizes your natural abilities. Work at having fun. Be more childlike. Stay in the present instead of thinking about the past or worrying about the future. It is a process that takes practice, time, and patience; it's a marathon, not a sprint. If you stick with it, your life will become more peaceful and contented.

ADD Medication

How does ADD medication work? I will focus on the category of medications known as amphetamines, which is a type of stimulant. These are the best type of drugs for ADD, and I don't prescribe others because they are poor substitutes. Although they are called stimulants, these medications actually slow down the thought processes in patients who have ADD. Their effect is immediate and dramatic. I have heard from virtually all my adolescent and adult patients with ADD who started on medication for the first time that it was like 'a switch being flipped,' or a 'shade being lifted'. It's a life-altering experience, like giving a legally blind person their first pair of glasses. In fact, if a patient does not have a dramatic reaction to starting medication, I question whether the diagnosis of ADD is correct. Medication is your friend, not your enemy!

When I was in medical school, asthma was diagnosed when a patient had persistent coughing and wheezing, temporarily improved by using an inhaler. Today, we recognize that most patients with asthma have a much milder form of the disease that is asymptomatic and undetectable except with exercise or a respiratory infection. We would not have recognized this mild form as asthma twenty-five years ago. Similarly, we only recognized ADD as the child (almost always a boy) who could not sit still in school. This was ADHD, but there was no such term back then. It is critical to realize that ADD, like all medical conditions, can be very mild to very severe. There is a spectrum or a continuum, if you will. It is not all or nothing. It is not yes or no.

Many medical professionals, educators, and parents fail to recognize mild forms of ADD, especially after elementary school. Even if it is recognized, it frequently isn't treated because of a misunderstanding of the condition, and of the medicines that we use to treat ADD. Many would say that the child doesn't have ADD, or doesn't need treatment, because they are getting good grades. Others would say that they don't want to start medications because they don't want to get their child addicted to the drugs. However, the amount of time and energy their child is expending in getting good grades can have a cost in the harm to their self-esteem and their willingness to take on new challenges.

Many of these children hit a wall eventually, and the milder the ADD, the longer it takes to hit that wall—whether in middle school, high school, college or beyond. It bears repeating: ADD is NOT all or nothing, just as high blood pressure or diabetes or asthma are not a simple positive or negative. Most people, including professionals, fail to understand this crucial principle.

Furthermore, drugs are not addictive; people are. Approximately ninety-five percent of people who drink alcohol and use prescription narcotics and benzodiazepines do not get addicted. People who have ADD need the medicine to calm their minds down, not to speed them up. There is no 'high' for these patients, nor do they want to get high. They just want to focus so they can get their work done. We overestimate the risks and underestimate the benefits of treatment with medication.

What about nonpharmacological compensatory strategies? Virtually all people with ADD develop some of these spontaneously through trial and error. Sometimes, parents and educators can help by eliminating obvious distractions and maximizing the studying environment. But that is like treating hypertension with diet and exercise: It may help temporarily, but eventually the patient will need medication if high blood pressure runs in the family. Compensatory measures are important, but medication may be necessary to reduce anxiety, enhance self-esteem, and encourage academic performance.

In addition, people who have ADD are disorganized and have trouble completing tasks and projects. Using a coach to help you get organized and encourage you to stay on task is a great tool. The coach can be a spouse, friend, or parent. The coach should be nurturing, positive, and consistent. This is a learning process that takes practice and time. You and your coach should recognize your successes and your progress, and always try to maintain a sense of humor. Laughter is therapeutic.

You are reading this book because you likely have unexplained anxiety or depression or are close to someone who does. You also may have recognized yourself in my explanations or stories. If so, I encourage you to go to either your primary care physician or psychotherapist and tell them you think you have ADD. Tell them why you think that you have it. If they are unwilling to explore the diagnosis with you, then you should consider getting a second opinion.

If you have ADD, ask your doctor to give you a prescription for a stimulant such as Ritalin or Adderall (not Strattera). If you have ADD and you try the medication, the effects should be immediate and life changing. I am not exaggerating. If you don't have an amazing 'aha!' experience, then you likely don't have ADD. If your doctor is reluctant to give you a prescription, ask to be referred to a psychologist (not a psychiatrist) to be tested for ADD. Remember to tell your doctor if ADD runs in the family with children, siblings, parents, or other family members. This will likely increase the chance of being correctly diagnosed with ADD.

For more strategies for living with ADD, I recommend a series of books written by Dr. Edward Hallowell, a psychiatrist who specializes in both child and adult ADD and ADHD. His first book, Driven to Distraction, is a classic in the field, and it is as relevant today as it was when it was written in 1994. I highly recommend it to my patients and their families who have been newly diagnosed with ADD. It is insightful, easy to read, and uplifting.

Chapter 7: Autism and Anxiety

We are just beginning to understand the mysteries of autism. We now recognize that it is a spectrum, ranging from very mild to very severe. Many theories exist about what causes autism, and how to treat autism. Most experts agree that there is a genetic, inherited basis of autism. It is not clear whether or not there is also an environmental trigger. Autism, like ADD, is a neurological condition in which parts of the brain develop differently than 'normal' brains. It is in the DNA of the children who have it. It is life-long and cannot be 'cured'.

As with ADD, the brain has a different operating system—an Apple instead of a PC, if you will. In order to understand how the autistic brain works, you need to read one or more books written by Temple Grandin. She is one of the first autistic people to enlighten us about how the autistic brain thinks and feels. Like ADD, autism runs in families, and can be mild, moderate or severe. Autism has existed for a long time. The term 'autism' was first introduced in 1910 and was first used clinically in 1938 by Hans Asperger. However, the symptoms of autism were recognized in the 1500s or earlier. Look at the family history: Are there children, parents, siblings, uncles, cousins, or even grandparents that might have autism or Asperger's Syndrome? Remember, it is a 'spectrum', not all or none.

Autism on the ADD Spectrum

I want to go out on a limb now. Could autism be on the same spectrum as ADD? I am not the first person to suggest this. We know that ADD is a 'busy' brain. But what if that brain went into overdrive? The thoughts and ideas come so fast that the person is focused on what is happening inside their mind. They cannot pay attention to what is happening right in front of them. When presented with conversation, instructions, or even physical stimulation, the person with autism becomes overwhelmed with too much information. They become frustrated because they cannot slow their mind enough to respond to the person trying to engage with them.

I have a patient who has two children on the autism spectrum. One child has Asperger's Syndrome and is high functioning; the other child has a more severe case of autism with frequent periods when she is agitated and inconsolable. My patient tells me that both have also been diagnosed with ADHD, as well. The father (my patient) is frustrated because he doesn't understand the difference and doesn't know where one condition leaves off and the other condition begins. He tells me that he is sure that he had ADHD as a child. I'm sure he still has it because you don't grow out of it. He thinks that he may be on the autism spectrum, as well, because he recognizes himself in some of his children's thoughts and behaviors. When I posed my theory about ADD/ADHD being on the mildest end of the autism spectrum, it totally resonated with him.

If ADD is a busy brain, autism is like pressing the gas pedal in the brain of that person. Instead of the thoughts racing a mile a minute, their thoughts are racing a mile per second! How could their brain respond appropriately to any form of outside information or stimulation—verbal, physical, or emotional—when their brain is already racing at the speed of light and they cannot slow it down? Frustration? Anger? Not listening? You bet.

Crying and rocking because you don't understand, and you can't make yourself understood? Of course. Oppositional or violent behavior? Not surprising.

The autistic brain is a busy brain, just like the ADD brain. As such, the autistic child may not sleep very much. The autistic brain processes information predominantly in the visual mode, as opposed to the auditory mode—in pictures rather than words. In addition, the primary problem in autism is language and communication. The autistic child hears and understands similarly to any other child but cannot speak the language that we speak. Consequently, they cannot make us understand what they are trying to communicate. It's as if they understand our English, but we don't understand their Martian! And they don't know why! They think that we do or should understand what they are trying to tell us.

Imagine the frustration of being unable to make yourself understood. It is no surprise that the child's behavior is sometimes angry or destructive, to themselves or to others. As an analogy, expressive aphasia is a neurological condition that is caused by a stroke in the speech center of the brain. Patients who have expressive aphasia understand what is being spoken. They process the information and formulate a response, but they cannot make their mouths speak the words. They may be able to say some words, or they make just make sounds that are not words. We cannot understand what they are trying to tell us. As an adult, it must be frustrating when you can't make yourself understood, even if you know that it is caused by a stroke. Imagine, now, how a child must feel if they can't get us to respond appropriately to them. They are 'talking'; why aren't we reacting?

Once parents understand this dynamic, they will be able to develop strategies to compensate for, and cope with, the communication and behavioral challenges with their autistic child. Special computers have been developed to help autistic children communicate from a very early age, even before they go to school. The more profound the autism, the more challenging the communication issue. By learning from mildly affected children, we can begin to formulate better strategies for managing severely affected children. I recently met the most delightful autistic boy.

*****

Scott is five years old. He looks like any other young boy. His parents brought him to see me for the first time in order to get some medication for his anger issues and aggressive behavior. Scott was happily playing with his toys, drinking his juice box, and eating his pretzels. And for most of the visit, he was 'talking'. That is, he was making sounds, but neither his parents nor I could understand his language. It was clear, though, that he understood ours. When his father asked him to sit down, he sat immediately. When his mother asked him if he wanted another juice box, he went into her bag and got it himself. And when he wanted a toy that he could not reach, he pointed to it. Since we were communicating with Scott, we responded appropriately to him and he was happy and content. I was fascinated and charmed by this little boy. He also exhibited some features of ADHD, constantly busy and moving from one activity to another and then back again.

*****

I explained to Scott's parents that ADD/ADHD and autism are likely on the same spectrum. Imagine having a busy brain, one that processes information in pictures and movies instead of words and stories. Now imagine having a busy brain on steroids. Warp speed! The faster the brain speed, the more introverted the child. He or she is watching a movie inside their brain and, therefore, is less responsive to outside stimulation. Now imagine that child when unwanted or noxious stimuli interrupts them, such as loud noises, a hug, or arguing adults. The child wants the unpleasantness to go away. How can the autistic child tell us? Any way that works. If we don't react to their language, they have learned that we react to their behavior. The child has learned what makes us respond.

The Autistic Child Becomes an Anxious Adult

As the autistic child becomes an adolescent and young adult, they may become anxious or depressed. This is especially true of the higher-functioning children who have Asperger's Syndrome. I recently saw a patient in his twenties who came to me because of anxiety.

*****

Daniel was 'on the spectrum' as diagnosed by his pediatrician and multiple psychiatrists. His mother told me that he had been given a dozen different diagnoses over the course of his life: Asperger's Syndrome, ADHD, OCD, Oppositional-Defiant, PTSD, bipolar, general anxiety disorder, social anxiety disorder, major depression, and more. Does Daniel have all of these 'diseases'? No. Daniel has one underlying cause of all of these symptoms: Asperger's Syndrome. This has resulted in his anxious and depressed mood, his ritualistic behavior to give order and comfort to his chaotic brain activity, his outbursts of anger and violence when he cannot make himself understood by those around him, his refusal to participate in activities that he knows he is incapable of doing at that time, and his mood swings. Daniel has been diagnosed with PTSD as a young adult because of his experiences living with Asperger's Syndrome.

*****

What can we do for Daniel and other young autistic people? First, we need to explain to them how their brains work. We need to emphasize that this is neurology, not psychology, and that their condition is not their fault; they were born with autism. By explaining autism to the autistic person, we can help them feel understood. We need to talk to Daniel as if he does not have autism. He understands everything. His inability to make us understand him causes his frustration. We need to try to help him express himself as best we can, with communication devices, hand signals, and pictures instead of words. Next, we need to find a skill or interest that Daniel is good at and then develop it. This may be a foundation that will give him a purpose and a routine, and even a job or career. Finally, we need to help Daniel by treating his PTSD, which he experiences as anxiety and depression. These strategies will improve his self-esteem. We can help him set realistic goals and feel successful by attaining them. In doing so, Daniel will feel like he is part of the community instead of being on the sidelines of life.

Asperger's Syndrome Also on The ADD Spectrum

We are just starting to recognize that there are adults with Asperger's Syndrome who have never been diagnosed earlier in their lives. Many are successful in their careers. They get married, have children, and seem to lead regular lives. However, they don't make eye contact, they seem emotionally distant, they don't like to be touched, and they hyper-focus on projects at work or home. Many of them were thought of as 'geeks', 'nerds', or 'weirdos' when they were growing up. However, once they found their niche, they became very successful in their field. I know many professionals who are college professors, doctors, actuaries, and executives at international social media companies who likely have Asperger's Syndrome. Most of these people don't know that they have Asperger's Syndrome!

My point is that like adult ADD, there is a group of adults who have never been diagnosed correctly because their condition is mild, and they appear successful and 'normal'. They may have sought professional help for their anxiety, depression, or insomnia. However, if the diagnosis is incorrect, then the treatment is likely to be ineffective or inadequate. By recognizing that autism is a neurological condition that is lifelong and can be mild enough to be undiagnosed into adulthood, we professionals can begin to make the correct diagnosis in our adult patients. We can then help them to understand how their condition affects their thoughts, emotions, and behaviors. Simply by explaining the facts, by telling them the story of their lives, the treatment of their anxiety and depression has begun.

I have written this chapter to highlight that anxiety frequently accompanies autism. A complete discussion of the thought processes, emotions, and behaviors in autism is beyond the scope of this book. I encourage you to read more about Asperger's Syndrome and the autism spectrum. My favorite autism book is *Thinking in Pictures* by Temple Grandin.

Chapter 8: Addiction and Substance Abuse

Like anxiety and depression, addiction is frequently a symptom of an underlying problem. The medical and mental health establishments view addiction as a 'disease'. The theory being that once someone is exposed to a substance of abuse, they can't stop using it. There is no 'off' switch. There are genetics at work, and addiction runs in the family. The easiest substance to illustrate this theory is alcohol. Once the alcoholic has that first drink, he will frequently drink until he passes out. The best solution is to not take that first drink. While this approach makes sense and applies to a small portion of people who have addictions, this scenario represents a minority of those affected by alcoholism and substance abuse.

Many people who 'abuse' substances and who become addicted are actually self-medicating. They are not getting high or trying to feel good; they are trying to numb the pain. What pain? Emotional pain. Alcohol and opiates work to numb the pain immediately, just as ibuprofen works to reduce physical pain. These people have chronic underlying anxiety, depression, and PTSD that may be unrecognized, undiagnosed, and inadequately treated. Sometimes, the patient will self-medicate instead of seeking medical treatment. But most often, they have sought treatment for their anxiety or depression. They have tried multiple antidepressant and antianxiety medications. They have tried psychotherapy, more than once, at different times in their lives. However, nothing works as well or as quickly as alcohol or opiates.

Addiction Is A Symptom

Why do patients self-medicate? Because it works! It is human nature to choose the quickest and most effective method to alleviate pain. At some point, many realize that short term pain relief is not a solution. They seek medical and/or psychological attention; however, psychotherapy is a painful and long-term process. Many people are unwilling, or unable, to face the difficult task involved in revisiting the underlying cause of their emotional pain. The pain of the status quo must be greater than the pain of change. Only then will a patient be motivated to fully engage in the process of therapy to treat their underlying depression, anxiety, and PTSD. That's why we often say that someone must hit bottom before they are ready to face their addiction. Change is hard. Facing your demons is hard. Voluntarily causing yourself emotional pain by revisiting your past is hard. It is much easier to numb the pain with alcohol or opiates.

What can we do? The most important principle to keep in mind is that addiction is usually a symptom and not a disease itself. Currently, professionals in addiction medicine focus almost exclusively on the details of addiction, recovery, and sobriety. Even in dual diagnosis centers, most treatments and therapies are based around the addiction itself, and very little time and attention are devoted to the underlying mental health issues. In fact, their view is that the addiction causes the anxiety and depression, not the other way around. They are incorrect: Anxiety and depression can lead to self-medication and addiction.

There is a disconnect in the mental health field. Some professionals will treat only addiction, while other professionals will treat only anxiety and depression. Traditional therapists will not treat people with addiction and substance abuse. Those who specialize in addiction will not treat patients who suffer from anxiety and depression. Mental health and addiction are connected and need to be treated simultaneously. Until we professionals recognize this, our approach and treatment of addiction will be misguided and ineffective.

Empathy for Those with Addictions

What more can we do? First and foremost, we as a society, as individuals, and as professionals must stop judging people with addictions. We need to be empathetic. We need to understand that the addiction is usually due to chronic and severe emotional pain.

Second, we need to confront each patient about the reason for their addiction to help them realize where their anxiety and depression are coming from. Many of them have PTSD due to emotional trauma in the past. They do not realize that the past is related to the present. They think that they have emotional scars, but they actually have open, festering emotional wounds. We professionals must do a better job of recognizing the underlying cause of the depressive and anxious symptoms of our patients. Once we identify the core of the problem, we can help our patients understand how their mind works to perpetuate the anxiety and depression. We can then help them use the cognitive, rational part of their brain to understand how the emotional part of their brain works.

The third step is to reframe or reinterpret the past trauma from a more objective and rational perspective. Specifically, to view the past from their inner Child perspective with the understanding and empathy from their Adult self. We can help to mature their inner Child by practicing this exercise in real life and in real time. This process takes time, effort, and guidance. The patient needs to understand that it will take many months of therapy to work through the process, but that they will have the chance to get their emotional health back.

Medication for Addiction

Sobriety and psychotherapy alone will not suffice to prevent the patient from relapsing. When we treat someone who has an addiction to alcohol or opiates, we need to use the same types of medications that we use for PTSD. These include antidepressants, anxiolytics, and mood stabilizers. It may also include medical marijuana. The patient is in emotional pain, and we must utilize tools that reduce the pain in the short term in order to prevent them from self-medicating. Medical marijuana is an effective alternative to alcohol and opiates in relieving the patient's pain without causing addiction. I will discuss medical marijuana in more detail in the chapters that follow.

Chapter 9: For Professionals
(and you as well)

My motivation in writing this book is to enlighten both patients with anxiety and depression, and the physicians, psychologists, and psychotherapists who care for them. In this chapter, I address those professionals who have chosen to treat mental health because I think that we need to do a better job of diagnosing and treating our patients. In doing so, we must start at the beginning and work towards the present, rather than starting with the present and working towards the beginning. The answer to the question "What is causing my anxiety and depression?" is found in the past, not in the present. In other words, we need to ascertain the original etiology of the patient's distress in order to understand the symptoms that cause them to seek treatment today.

Getting to the Root Cause

The anxiety and depression that brings the patient to our office is frequently caused by emotional trauma that occurred in childhood or early adulthood. The patient may not have made this connection, but we should look for it at the first appointment. Many of my patients who do not have situational anxiety or depression know where their distress comes from, and they are willing to tell me. In fact, they have been waiting, wishing, and praying for someone to ask them the correct questions so that they can finally unburden themselves. But there are certain conditions that each of them requires before they are willing to share their feelings.

First, they must sense that you genuinely care about them. We professionals must view our patients as people first and 'diseases' second. Many of my physician colleagues treat diseases, without enough consideration of the people who have them! Professionals, we need to look our patients in the eye and feel empathy for them. We need to make them feel safe, comfortable, and cared for. Our concern should be obvious to our patients. As professionals, we set the tone of the relationship. If we are clinical and distant, our patients will likely hold back vital information. They will not trust just anyone with their deepest and darkest secrets and fears. The information that the patient volunteers is just the tip of the iceberg. Unfortunately, most times the focus of the therapy never gets much deeper.

Asking the Correct Questions

Second, we must ask the correct questions. We cannot wait for our patients to give us the information spontaneously. I start the conversation with an open-ended question: "Why are you anxious?" Or, "Why are you depressed?" If they tell me that they are having marital or work-related problems, for example, I believe them, and we talk about what specifically is making them anxious or depressed. The emotional reaction is appropriate to the environmental stressor.

When my patient tells me that they don't know why they are anxious or depressed, or if their anxiety or depression is out of proportion to their situational stress, my antenna goes up. At this point, I usually ask them what is bothering them: What do they think about when they let their mind wonder? It is one of my favorite questions and techniques because the patient subconsciously goes right there. Many times, they will tell me that they don't know, even when they do. They are testing me. Will I let it go? Can they trust me? They make me come and get it.

I ask, "What do you think about when you aren't focused on anything in particular? When you are driving? When you are in the shower? When you are watching a TV show that isn't very interesting?" I have them thinking, now, and the subconscious thoughts and feelings are rising to the level of consciousness. But they won't let themselves reveal the answer. Then I go in for the kill. I tell them that I want to ask them an off-the-wall question. "Did you have any emotional trauma when you were younger? No one gets to be twenty-one without some emotional scars—what are your emotional scars from your childhood?"

At this point my patient will reveal the true etiology of their anxiety or depression. In most cases, they could not connect the dots between their past and present because they sincerely believe that their past emotional trauma is all behind them. They don't realize that what they have is not a scar but rather a festering, pus-filled wound that had risen to the surface and demands attention. It is our job to uncover that wound and lance it so that the pus can be drained, and the healing can begin.

Don't Peel the Onion

In my experience, mental health professionals are not aggressive enough in getting to the cause of our patients' emotional pain. They take the approach of peeling the onion. They start at the present, the outside, and peel off layer after layer until they get to the core. Since Sigmund Freud, psychiatrists, psychologists, and psychotherapists have been taught this basic principle of psychotherapy. It has been institutionalized and is universal among therapists. I think this is a fundamental mistake in our approach to mental health. We must identify the etiology of the symptoms quickly, in the first session, if possible. We must make the correct diagnosis. Then we can focus on treating the anxiety, depression, and PTSD.

There is a fatal flaw in the current technique of peeling the onion: The patient and the therapist get stuck in the outer layers! Most times, the core—the source of emotional distress— is never revealed. Classic psychoanalysis takes years to complete. Today, most patients who seek treatment will only go to therapy for weeks or months. This might be satisfactory for situational anxiety and depression. However, we need a different approach for the patients whose symptoms stem from underlying, undiagnosed PTSD and ADD. Specifically, we need to start with the answer, and then see how it causes the anxiety and depression that the patient is experiencing now.

Modern psychotherapy attempts to identify the symptoms and classify the 'disorder'. Most of the treatment consists of searching for the answer by understanding the specific experiences described by the patient. While we may understand how anxiety or depression was caused in those experiences, we fail to see the forest through the trees, i.e., the bigger picture. "Why do I get anxious about everything and nothing?" Until we answer the fundamental question that allows the patient to understand how their brain functions, their generalized anxiety will continue to be perceived as random. They need the story that connects the episodes and that explains why anxiety is their 'default' mode.

Look to Your Patient's Childhood

What I am proposing is heresy! But we professionals have forgotten Psychology 101. The pioneers of psychologic theory knew the importance of childhood experiences in creating the emotional health and illness of the adult person. The current emphasis in mental health is on brain chemistry being out of balance. This may be true, but I would submit that the imbalance is the result of, not the cause of, anxiety and depression. We have neglected to investigate and explore the most basic and most important factor in emotional health: The patient's childhood experiences. For you therapists reading this book, think about how often you talk about formative childhood events with your patients. Not often, if at all. For you patients reading this book, think about the therapy you have had. How often did you talk about meaningful childhood emotional traumas? Not often. Once we determine that our patients are anxious and or depressed, we need to analyze whether the cause is situational or generalized. If it is situational, is the anxiety or depression proportional to the situation? If the symptoms are greater than we would expect for a given situation, or if the symptoms are not situational, we need to take a look at their childhood.

We need to be confrontational with our patients, but in an empathetic way. "Nobody gets to twenty-one years old without some emotional scars. Did anything happen to you when you were younger that caused you emotional distress?" If the patient trusts you and feels that you are caring and competent, they will frequently give you the answer. If not, then we need to keep asking questions about their childhood until we get a sense of their experiences growing into adulthood. "Tell me about your childhood." "How did you do in school?" "What was it like growing up in your household?" Take a history. Explore relationships and important experiences. If the patient reveals important information, the next question should be, "How did that affect you?"

The Patient's Reaction

I observe a physical reaction virtually every time I make the correct diagnosis of PTSD or ADD. At the start of the visit, the patient may be talkative, animated, and perhaps slightly nervous. They tell me about their anxiety or depression as they understand it. I ask them probing questions and they frequently start crying. I consider this a therapeutic cry, and I know that we are on the right track. I tell them my diagnosis of PTSD or ADD. I explain to them that their emotional trauma when they were younger has created the anxiety and depression that they are experiencing now. I show them that their patterns of thinking and feeling have not changed from the time of their emotional trauma.

During my explanation, their body language dramatically changes, and I know that I my assessment is accurate. First, they get very quiet. They stop talking, and they are perfectly still. Their breathing slows and they make eye contact. I have their undivided attention, and they are listening intently. I am telling them a story that they have never heard before, and it explains everything. They are calm and relieved because for the first time, their symptoms—and their lives——make sense to them.

Then they start talking again. They tell me more details about their traumatic event. They recognize how their emotions now are similar to what they felt in the past. They begin to fill in the timeline of their earlier lives when life's challenges caused similar anxiety and distress. It is as if they are watching a movie of their own life unfold before their eyes! When I see the patient at the next visit, their demeanor is very different than at the initial visit. They are more relaxed and focused, and very much in the present instead of thinking about the past or worrying about the future. Now the real work can begin with their psychotherapist.

The patient does not realize that their past relates to their present condition. "That's over. I've moved on." We need to take our patients back to the beginning. Once we uncover the original source of distress—underachieving because of ADD, a divorce or death in the family, bullying at school, or verbal abuse at home— we can begin to see and understand a lifelong pattern of thinking and feeling that has caused the patient's current anxiety or depression.

There is the IQ and the EQ—the Adult and the Child, the rational brain and the emotional brain. There is a disconnect between them. The rational Adult has moved on, but the emotional Child is stuck at the age at which the trauma of childhood occurred. The Child has been ignored and despised by the Adult for a long time. Now the Adult must go the other way and listen to, embrace, and forgive the Child. This process takes time, practice, and assistance from the therapist in order to emotionally mature the Child, and to help the EQ match the IQ.

Practical Techniques

I am not a psychotherapist; I consider my role to be a diagnostician. While I refer my patients to mental health professionals for psychotherapy, I also use several therapeutic techniques that are easy to conceptualize and resonate with patients. I point out that my patient's emotional growth has been stunted, and that they are stuck at the age at which their emotional trauma occurred. The Adult is their rational self; the Child is their emotional self. The therapy and treatment allow the older self to help the younger self grow up by literally talking to their younger self: Accepting him, forgiving him, nurturing him, and loving him. Tell him that he did the best job he could in the situation that he was in. He should be proud of himself for all that he has been able to accomplish in spite of the bad 'hand of cards' he was dealt. Tell him that it is OK to come out and play, to have fun, and to trust again. It takes practice and it takes time, but if the patient can follow this process, their emotional trauma loses power.

I also find that journaling and group therapy are very effective. Journaling allows patients to vomit their emotions of their young self all over the page. Cry, scream, and curse; let the emotions out. Aim them at the cause—parents, bullies, or just life. This journal is not to be shared with anyone. It is a way to exorcize the emotions in an effective, safe, and satisfying way. By journaling, the patient can indulge their emotions when they need to, and then box them up and put them in a closet until they need to explore them again. This also helps facilitate the conversation between the IQ and the EQ—between the thoughts and emotions. It allows them to express the fear, pain, guilt, embarrassment, helplessness, anger, and frustration of the Child. Only then can the Adult help the Child understand that whatever happened was not the Child's fault and comfort the Child with unconditional acceptance, praise, and love.

Group therapy is invaluable yet underutilized. The most important benefits of group therapy are the safe and empathetic environment in which each person can express their feelings, and the understanding that they are not alone. Another major benefit of group therapy is that it teaches both sides of communication: Speaking and listening. You must first be honest to communicate with yourself. Then make sure that the other person understands what you are trying to tell them. It is not what you say, but rather what the other person hears. Furthermore, your listening skills will be sharpened by understanding what that person is trying to tell you.

<u>Look for the Story Line</u>

To recap, the three essential elements a patient requires from us are caring, competency, and trust. Ascertain whether the patient's anxiety or depression is situational. If not, or if the emotional reaction is out of proportion to the situation, explore the patient's childhood and early adulthood emotional experiences, hopefully at the first visit. Look for experiences in their past that could indicate underlying PTSD due to an emotionally catastrophic event or if life at home or school was like a war zone, where they faced danger, insecurity, and fear day after day.

Patients with PTSD have a pattern of negative thinking that underscores many of their choices and behaviors. Look for the patterns and try to point them out to the patient. Show them how the PTSD caused by their childhood emotional trauma affects their thoughts, emotions, and behaviors today. Recognize that adult ADD is real. Look for it as a possible cause of the patient's anxiety and depression. Taking a family history is a good place to start. If any of their children have ADD, then the child got it from one of the parents and therefore there's a fifty percent chance that your patient has ADD.

Finally, we as human beings have a fundamental need to hear the 'story' that explains our world and our place in it. We love to read novels, watch television, and view movies because they are all stories. By vicariously experiencing someone else's story, we hope to understand more about ourselves. For patients who have non-situational anxiety, their lives do not make sense; there is no explanation, pattern, or continuity. Life is random, chaotic, and frightening. When I am able to tell a patient the story of their life, it suddenly makes sense! If they can understand their own story, then they can begin to have more control over their lives. They can begin to make the rest of their lives more like the type of life that they truly want, with our help.

Chapter 10: Tying It All Together

It is my sincere hope that I have started a conversation about the prevalence and importance of PTSD and ADD that is unrecognized by both patients and professionals. We need to recognize that there are individuals who are functioning in society, but who are still suffering the effects of emotional trauma that occurred when they were younger. They have PTSD causing anxiety and depression that is impairing their quality of life. Once a patient has PTSD, it never goes away. There will be exacerbations and remissions, but their anxiety or depression is always just below the surface, lurking in their subconscious, waiting to be triggered by a memory or an experience. We can manage PTSD, but we can't 'cure' it.

We need to recognize that ADD is a lifelong condition that can be mild enough that it is not diagnosed until adulthood. We cannot discount the diagnosis of ADD just because the patient has been successful up until this point. Their success has come at a cost. Undiagnosed or untreated ADD can lead to anxiety and depression in both children and adults.

If you suffer from anxiety and/or depression that is generalized and is not in reaction to a current stressful experience, revisit your past. You have likely not 'gotten over it'. It is not a scar, but rather a festering wound that you have submerged into your subconscious when your life became busy with school, work, or raising a family. Now that you do not have to devote all of your attention to your daily life, your unresolved emotional conflicts are bubbling up to the surface in the form of anxiety and depression.

You find yourself thinking or feeling about specific events that happened when you were younger—while you are driving, when you are in the shower, or when you are not paying attention to the television show that you are watching. Where does your mind go when it is allowed to wander? That is what is bothering you. What are your bad dreams and nightmares about? That is the root cause of your PTSD. Do not ignore your thoughts and feelings. Do not self-medicate with alcohol or narcotics. Seek help from your family physician, a psychologist, or a psychotherapist, and start the visit with the statement, "I think that I have PTSD from…" If you state that you have anxiety or depression, you will likely get treated for those symptoms, and the underlying diagnosis of PTSD will not be made. Doctors and therapists need you to make them aware of your diagnosis because they have not been taught how to recognize milder forms of PTSD. Hopefully, as more and more of you patients seek therapy, more professionals will recognize how common PTSD is, and we will become better at making the diagnosis in our patients.

Adults with a Recent Diagnosis of ADD

If you are an adult with ADD, it is not too late to be treated. If you are suffering from anxiety or depression because you are overwhelmed, disorganized, or falling behind at work, you may have ADD. It is not a cliché; it is real. Do not feel embarrassed or worry about what other people in your life will say or think about you. You have been successful in life to this point, but the world has changed! We now live in a world where most jobs require computer skills, test taking for certifications, and multi-tasking. When you started your career as a real estate agent, auto mechanic, HVAC technician, or cosmetologist, most of your learning was hands-on experience. Your skill was demonstrated every day on the job. But now you have to take exams to be 'certified'. The paperwork is endless. Performing the work is only part of the job. You gravitated to your profession because it highlighted your cognitive strengths, and minimized your weaknesses caused by your ADD. Now you are expected to perform functions that were never required in the past. You may need medication to help you accurately demonstrate your knowledge and skill.

You do not have to be handicapped by your ADD. You should get the medicine you need to use as a tool to continue to function productively and without anxiety. Medication for ADD will help you focus, finish your tasks, and help you reduce your anxiety by allowing you to keep up with the pace of your work. When you finish today's work, you won't be anxious about unfinished projects that will prevent you from finishing tomorrow's work. When you can focus on completing the administrative part of your job, you won't be anxious about new requirements or certifications.

Adults Diagnosed with ADD in Childhood, but Not Treated

If you are an adult who knows that you had ADD growing up but were not treated with medication, it's not too late to get help. When you were younger, there was a lot of controversy about whether or not ADD was real, or just a 'fad' diagnosis. Doctors and parents were in a quandary about who to treat and when to treat it. If you were doing well in school, you were likely not on medication. You didn't need it. Except that it took you twice as long to do your homework. You got B's and C's when you know that you could do A work. You procrastinated and then crammed when you had a test or a paper that was due. You avoided certain classes or subjects because you knew that they would be too hard.

You pretended not to care, or you just didn't try, so that mediocre grades were not a reflection of your intelligence. Except that your self-esteem suffered. You may have felt inadequate or 'different'. These emotional reactions to your ADD may have caused anxiety and depression when you were younger and may be causing PTSD now. That's right: The anxiety and depression that you have now is from PTSD caused by living with untreated ADD. In this instance, just treating the ADD with medications is not going to adequately treat your anxiety and depression today. You need psychotherapy to revisit your past, so that you can evaluate your life's experiences and decisions based on your new-found knowledge.

You were not, and are not, stupid. It wasn't your fault. With the help of a good therapist who understands that you have PTSD, and with the help of medications for anxiety, depression, and ADD, you can make the rest of your life better. Start a new chapter—one with more understanding of how your brain works. Pay attention to how and why you make decisions, what activities accent your cognitive strengths and minimize your weaknesses, and how to reduce your anxiety with and without ADD medication.

Professionals

If you are a physician, psychologist, or psychotherapist, thank you for reading this book. Once you begin to look for PTSD or ADD as the cause of your patients' anxiety and depression, you will realize how prevalent and pervasive they are. We professionals have been frustrated by the lack of successful treatment, and thus, the persistence of anxiety and depression in our patients. I am certain that once we start making the correct underlying diagnosis, the efficacy of our treatment will vastly improve. Not only will our patients benefit, but we professionals will get more satisfaction from our work due to the positive effects of our new approach.

Once we start treating undiagnosed PTSD and ADD and stop treating only the symptoms of anxiety and depression, our patients will have better outcomes. It is essential that we explore the early childhood and adolescent experiences of every one of our patients, unless it is clear that they have situational anxiety or depression. No one gets to twenty-one without emotional trauma. All of us have scars; however, when anxiety is generalized and long-standing, it suggests that there is an open wound, not a scar. The combination of the severity of the emotional trauma with the sensitivity of the developing brain at the time of the trauma, can create the perfect storm that results in PTSD in adulthood.

Our patients were in survival mode, scanning for danger and always waiting for the next disaster to occur. And they still are in this mode of never letting their guard down, always worrying, never allowing themselves to be happy and trusting nothing and no one. We must go back to the beginning with our patients, and then work up to the present. There is a pattern of negativity that is the 'default' mode for their thoughts and emotions. It explains why they are anxious or depressed now, and why they have been anxious or depressed for most of their lives. When we explain this pattern, we can help 'connect the dots', and enable them to understand the 'story' of their lives. It makes sense to them, and it will calm them, because their anxiety or depression is not random.

When a patient worries about everything and nothing at all, I suspect that underlying PTSD is the cause. I ask them directly, "Has anyone told you that you grind your teeth at night? Do you have TMJ syndrome?" If a patient has fibromyalgia, I shock them when I tell them that they sleep in the fetal position, causing their muscles to ache the next day. How did I know? It is one of the physical manifestations of PTSD. Most of my patients didn't realize how they slept until I pointed it out.

If we continue to practice using the current model of starting with the present and working backwards, we will fail to reach the origin of their symptoms because we will get stuck, distracted, and bogged down. We must change our practice methods, and we must teach our students to start at the center and work outwards. If there is a history of anxiety and depression, or if the anxiety and depression are out of proportion to the current situation, then it is incumbent upon us to explore the patient's childhood.

The 'answer' should not come at the end of therapy—it should start at the beginning. Then the psychotherapy can be therapeutic immediately! Instead of searching for the answer, session after session, you can search for understanding in light of the underlying cause. Instead of random events and experiences, both you and the patient can begin to see patterns of thoughts, emotions, and behaviors.

I often write my patients a prescription for FUN. I tell them to be more childlike, because in childhood, yesterday never happened, and tomorrow is never coming. Many patients didn't have a true childhood; they deserve to have one now. It is not enough that the activity is enjoyable; they need to allow themselves to have fun doing it! It may sound intuitive, but patients with PTSD have not allowed themselves to have fun in a very long time. It takes a conscious effort to stop worrying. It takes practice, repetition, and time to learn to be childlike if you have PTSD.

Medical Marijuana

If you are a physician, we have a new tool to treat PTSD and the symptoms of anxiety and depression: Medical marijuana. Canada and California have been using legal medical marijuana for over fifteen and twenty years respectively. Thirty-three states and the District of Columbia have legalized medical marijuana. The reason is not because it generates tax revenue; it's because it works.

Clinically, marijuana turns the brain off during sleep so that patients can rest instead of processing their emotional trauma in their nightmares. A good night sleep is undervalued. Patients who have anxiety and PTSD sleep poorly. They have difficulty falling asleep and staying asleep because they cannot turn off their minds. They have chronic fatigue, just like patients with sleep apnea. Medical marijuana is more effective, and has less side effects than traditional sleeping pills, muscle relaxants, and antianxiety medication. By relaxing the patient's mind and body, they have a restful sleep. They awaken more relaxed, with more energy, and in a better mood. They are less anxious, and less susceptible to mood swings throughout the day.

Furthermore, I have found that medical marijuana used during the day helps patients to stay focused and 'in the present'. The patient stops worrying and is less anxious. I am not referring to 'pot', and I am not suggesting that patients get 'high'. Marijuana can be processed into oils that create beneficial effects without cognitive impairment. The patient's performance actually improves because their anxiety is gone. This beneficial effect is magnified in patients who have ADD. Medical marijuana slows down the racing brain which reduces anxiety and frustration. In adults with ADD, it is an excellent alternative to traditional medications. In children with autism, it can be life-changing for both the child and the parents.

The Future

I am very optimistic about the future treatment of patients with chronic, non-situational anxiety and depression. When I explain to my patients where their anxiety and depression comes from, it makes sense to them. They embrace the diagnosis. They are relieved that there is an 'answer'. They are willing to explore and treat their condition anew, with understanding and hope. They begin to see patterns of PTSD and ADD in their family and close friends, and they share their insights with them so that they, too, can seek help. As with many reforms, it begins at the grass roots with common people bringing the conversation to the general public, professionals, and the media. It is my fervent hope that a transformation in mental health care has begun. In the appendixes that follow, I invite you to read more stories about people with PTSD and ADD. The patients and their stories are real, but some of the details have been changed to preserve their anonymity.

Appendix A: PTSD Stories

Lucy, Age 40: An Alcoholic

Lucy is a forty-year-old woman who comes to me because she is afraid that she is becoming an alcoholic. She starts drinking when she comes home from work, and sometimes, she drinks until she passes out. Recently, Lucy has the desire to drink during the day. She is an alcoholic. Like most people who are addicted to alcohol or drugs, she is self-medicating her emotional pain.

When Lucy was thirty-two, she was diagnosed with cancer. It was discovered early, treated, and cured. For Lucy, getting cancer was like being struck by lightning—it came out of the blue, and she was emotionally unprepared for it. She worries every day about when the cancer is going to come back. The fear and the anxiety are always there, despite medication and psychotherapy. Alcohol numbs the emotional pain, but Lucy feels worse when the effects wear off. She feels helpless and depressed that she can't control her emotions, and it is ruining the quality of her life.

At my suggestion, Lucy has started to use medical marijuana. Since the marijuana has been effective, she has no need to self-medicate with alcohol. Lucy has been sober for six months, and I am hopeful about her future. She is sleeping better every night, and she is focused during the day. She is no longer thinking about the past and worrying about the future.

Addiction is widely misunderstood by most professionals and nonprofessionals. Almost every alcoholic or drug-addicted patient that I have seen has PTSD. When I share this observation with those in recovery, there is unanimous agreement about themselves and their peers. In order to successfully combat addiction, we must first recognize the underlying PTSD that led to the addiction. If we do not soothe the emotional pain, in addition to addressing the alcohol or drug addiction, it will be difficult to keep them from self-medicating.

Medical marijuana is extremely effective in treating PTSD that has been resistant to more traditional medications. It has fewer adverse effects than alcohol, opiates, and benzodiazepines. Medical marijuana is not addictive, and it is not a gateway drug to other substances of abuse, contrary to popular beliefs. There are many strains that are effective without causing cognitive impairment or getting 'high'. It works during the day by helping the patient stay in the present, avoid thinking about the past, and worrying about the future. It works at night by reducing the dreams and nightmares so that the patient can get a restful sleep.

Susan, Age 41: Will Lightening Strike Twice?

Susan is a forty-one-year-old accountant who comes to see me because the medications she has been taking are not controlling her anxiety. She is on four different medications, including an antidepressant, a mood stabilizer, an antianxiety medication, and a sleeping pill. She is nervous during the day and she cannot sleep at night, in spite of her polypharmacy. I immediately suspect that she has PTSD. I ask Susan if she had any emotional trauma when she was younger. She tells me that she was in a head-on motor vehicle accident when she was twenty-one. She was thrown from the car and almost died but was fortunate that there were no life-threatening injuries—just a broken pelvis. She was unable to walk for three months. Susan tells me that she is having flashbacks and nightmares about the accident.

I tell Susan that she has PTSD causing her anxiety. She needs to explore her feelings with a psychotherapist, and she should get a journal to allow twenty-one-year-old Susan to ventilate her feelings of fear, guilt, and helplessness. Medication without therapy will not manage her anxiety and PTSD. Susan is relieved and comforted by my diagnosis. She begins to cry because for the first time, she is able to understand why she has anxiety. It makes sense and it is not random.

Commentary

Lightning struck for Susan when she was twenty-one. There was life before the accident, and a different life after the accident. She had a near-death experience. Since the accident, Susan is waiting for lightning to strike again. She is scanning for danger, always vigilant and looking over her shoulder waiting for the next unforeseen trauma to occur. She is fearful, anxious, and insecure. She needs both medication and psychotherapy to manage her emotions and to put them in perspective.

At forty-one years old, Susan's life is more stable than it was when she was younger, when she was focused on her career and young family. Her subconscious memories and emotions have risen to the level of her consciousness and are causing her PTSD symptoms to intensify. Susan needs to reduce her thinking about the past and worrying about the future by starting a new hobby or activity that she can focus on in the present. By giving her mind something objective to pay attention to, her subconscious will quiet down, and her rational brain will be in control of her emotional brain once again.

Eileen, Age 36: TMJ syndrome and Chronic Headaches

Eileen is a thirty-six-year-old dentist who comes to see me because she has diagnosed herself with TMJ syndrome. She has headaches every day, even though she uses a custom mouth guard. She thinks that she may have a brain tumor. I order an MRI and it is normal. Eileen has tenderness at the temporal-mandibular joint, and her jaw clicks when she opens her mouth. I ask her if she sleeps in the fetal position with her body clenched. She responds that she does, and how did I know that? TMJ syndrome and fibromyalgia frequently occur together. TMJ syndrome occurs because the patient clenches their teeth during sleep; fibromyalgia occurs because they clench their body during sleep. When a patient has both, it is likely that PTSD is the cause.

I ask Eileen if she had any emotional traumas when she was growing up. She tells me that her father was diagnosed with cancer when she was in elementary school, and that he died shortly thereafter. I ask Eileen how that affected her life. She tells me that her family had to move and that she had to change schools. She remembers that she felt insecure until high school when she got involved in both academics and after-school activities. She was successful in college and dental school, but her anxiety has increased since having children. Eileen feels overwhelmed and fearful. She cannot concentrate at work, and she cannot get a good night sleep. She worries all of the time, and her worrying is out of proportion to the situation.

I tell Eileen that she has PTSD causing her TMJ, anxiety, and insomnia. Her emotional memories are likely triggered by having young children, causing her to remember her own childhood. I prescribed a mild antidepressant and an antianxiety medication. She has an appointment with a psychologist. I tell Eileen to start the conversation with, "I have PTSD from my childhood." We agree to meet again in a month to reevaluate her physical and emotional symptoms.

Commentary

No one gets to twenty-one without some emotional scars. For those with PTSD, they have open wounds that have not scarred over. Most people with PTSD think that the past is behind them and that their emotional conflicts from their childhood, adolescence, or young adulthood have been resolved. When their anxiety and fears resurface years later, they are unaware that it is related to their previous emotional trauma. When I 'connect the dots' for them, they are relieved. I explain how their feelings now are similar to the feelings they had when they were younger. An event triggers an emotional memory, which triggers the feelings of anxiety and insecurity. We must return to the time when the initial trauma occurred so that we can listen to the younger self. By understanding their Child, the Adult and the psychotherapist can explore and reframe the events and emotions of the past so that they have less power.

Frequently, patients come to my office with physical symptoms such as headaches, body aches, and abdominal pain. If I cannot identify a physical source of their symptoms, I look for an emotional cause. The pain is real; it is not 'psychosomatic'. Emotional distress causes physical reactions that result in medical conditions such as TMJ syndrome, fibromyalgia, and irritable bowel syndrome. If you have been diagnosed with one of these conditions, you should explore the possibility that you may have PTSD causing your anxiety or depression.

Christine, Age 28: Still Suffering from Childhood Abuse

Christine is a twenty-eight-year-old woman who has PTSD causing her anxiety and depression. She came to see me at her psychologist's suggestion to get a prescription for medication. She tells me that she has PTSD from a bad relationship that started three years ago and ended with a restraining order. Christine has been in psychotherapy for the past six months. She likes her psychologist who made the correct diagnosis.

I ask Christine if she had anxiety before she started her previous relationship. She tells me that her symptoms started when she was fifteen. "What made you anxious?" Her dad was emotionally and physically abusive. He was critical of her looks and behavior. He made fun of her and her brother. He stood in the doorway of her room, physically blocking it, and berated her. When her dad became angry, he struck and pushed his children. He was a bully! Her mother was abused and submissive to her husband, unable to help herself or her children.

Chronic bullying at home created Christine's PTSD long before she met the boyfriend who would abuse her. Christine grew up in an emotional war zone of fear, insecurity, and helplessness. I pointed out how the relationship with her boyfriend was remarkably similar to the relationship with her father. For financial reasons, she still lives at home with her parents. I told Christine that she is still living in a war zone. She is still in survival mode. In order to treat her PTSD, she must move out as soon as possible.

Commentary

Christine is fortunate that she chose a therapist who recognizes and understands PTSD. However, the psychologist incorrectly identified the failed relationship between Christine and her boyfriend as the cause of her PTSD. When you start with the current symptoms and work backwards, psychotherapy may focus on a recent emotionally traumatic event. In Christine's case, the tumultuous relationship with her boyfriend could have caused her PTSD.

When asked, Christine identified the true etiology of her emotional trauma: Her father, the bully. If I had not asked her about having anxiety in childhood or adolescence, Christine would not have recognized or volunteered the earlier trauma. Home was a war zone for her. Furthermore, she entered a relationship with a man who abused her just as her father did! We need to start at the beginning and work forward—from childhood until the present—in order to see the pattern of PTSD.
When we correctly identify the root cause of anxiety, fear, and helplessness, we can understand the decisions and events that

have occurred throughout a patient's life. Each person has a story. It is essential to uncover the origin of that story. When we can explain their life story to them, the patient is relieved because their current symptoms make sense! Their life is not as random and chaotic as they thought. We can reframe their emotional trauma to help them see that whatever happened was not their fault—they were in survival mode. Now the psychotherapy can begin.

An essential part of PTSD treatment is to avoid the people, places, and things that might perpetuate or trigger the symptoms. Christine cannot begin to heal if she continues to live at home with her parents. She remains in survival mode because she is in emotional danger. Until Christine leaves 'the scene of the crime', she will not be able to start a new chapter in her life— one that is less anxious, fearful, and helpless.

Sam, Age 55: Suffering in Silence

Sam has anxiety and insomnia. He knows that he has ADD, but he has never required medication. He works in sales and is successful in his work and in his personal life. Internally, Sam struggles with anxiety that appears randomly during the day, and a busy brain that wakes him every night. He frequently has nightmares. I ask Sam about his childhood. He tells me that he was raised by strict, religious parents who believed that corporal punishment prevented a child from becoming spoiled. Both parents were emotionally distant, and he was frequently beaten with a belt.

Sam does not appear to be anxious. He is confident and in control of his emotions, yet his affect seems blunted. He is inappropriately mild mannered—neither angry nor sad when he should be. I suspect that he does not become excited or happy either. I tell Sam that he has PTSD from his upbringing. Home was not an emotionally safe place. Punishment was random and disproportionate to his behavior. He was likely 'walking on eggshells', trying to behave in order to avoid confrontation. He did not feel safe because at any time, unprovoked, he could be disciplined and beaten with the belt.

Sam's current anxiety comes from waiting for the next punishment that will come unexpectedly and undeservedly—not from his parents, but rather from life. The feelings are subconscious and arise when his conscious mind is not engaged in his work or activities. They cause his nightmares that wake him from sleep. Sam has PTSD. He will accept medications for his symptoms of anxiety and insomnia, but he declines my advice of psychotherapy. I understand.

Commentary

Revisiting the past is difficult and painful. Sam's PTSD is mild because it has not significantly affected his ability to feel successful and in control of his life. At fifty-five, he is satisfied to treat his symptoms of anxiety and insomnia. That is appropriate for Sam because most of the time, his rational brain is in control of his emotional brain.

For many people who seek help for their anxiety, depression, and insomnia, their PTSD is more severe. When the emotional Child is in control of the rational Adult, treating the symptoms of PTSD with medication without psychotherapy will often fail. Most patients need to understand where and how their feelings originated, and how their feelings of anxiety, fear, and helplessness are the same now as they were then. They need to recognize, understand, and forgive their inner Child. The Adult and the Child must work together and make peace with each other in order to reduce the power of their PTSD.

Ann, Age 25: A Panic Attack Waiting to Happen

Ann came to see me because she had her first panic attack. She went to the emergency room because of chest pains, palpitations, and shortness of breath. She thought that she was having a heart attack at twenty-five-years-old. The medical evaluation was normal. Ann was correctly diagnosed with a panic attack.

When I saw her in follow-up from the ER, she was visibly anxious and fidgeting in her seat. She could not talk without crying. I asked Ann what was happening in her life? What was wrong with her situation? Was it her job? Her boyfriend? A sick relative? "No. Everything is fine." Could it be something that happened when you were younger that was triggered by something that happened recently? "Yes. This month is the two-year anniversary of my sister's death. She committed suicide by hanging herself, and I didn't see it coming. I thought that I was dealing with it well, but obviously I am not. I never really grieved because my parents were so distraught that I did not want to upset them with my problems. I think about my sister every day. I never should have let her kill herself."

I told Ann that I was sorry that she had to live with this burden alone for so long. She has PTSD from the emotional trauma. Lightning struck out of the blue. There was her life before the suicide, and a different life since then. Her anxiety, depression, and guilty feelings are understandable and appropriate. They are the cause of her panic attacks. I told Ann that she is not responsible for her sister's suicide. It was not her fault. When a person is in so much emotional pain that they take their own life, no one can prevent it. If she had somehow managed to stop her sister that day, she would have found a different way or a different day to kill herself. It is difficult to commit suicide, especially in a violent way. Unlike an intentional overdose, hanging yourself is not impulsive. Her sister must have been in a tremendous amount of emotional pain to have planned and gone through with her suicide. No one could have stopped her.

Commentary

Ann did not recognize where her emotions were coming from. Her PTSD seems obvious as you read her story, but many patients suppress their subconscious and are not self-aware. They may think that the past is behind them, and that the past has nothing to do with their emotional state in the present. Ann did not tell me her story. I had to ask her questions to reveal the source of her distress. She was not intentionally keeping the information from me. She didn't realize that she had an emotional open wound instead of a scar. If I had given Ann medications for her panic attack without understanding the etiology of her anxiety, I would not have been doing my job.

When lightning strikes unexpectedly, and when a person is young and emotionally vulnerable, PTSD is frequently the result. This is a transformational experience where there is one life before, and a very different life afterwards. We cannot change the past. With psychotherapy, we can help the patient understand rationally and objectively how this event created their anxiety, depression, and guilty feelings. When we help them to believe that the trauma was not their fault, the patient will begin to forgive themselves and will start to heal.

Mary, Age 63: Older Young Mary

Mary came to see me with her daughter because she has fibromyalgia. She has had body aches and fatigue for over twenty years. Her recent medical evaluation by her rheumatologist revealed no other diagnosis to explain her symptoms, but she is sick and tired of being sick and tired! I confirmed her diagnosis by verifying that she clenched her body and her teeth while she slept. I explained that most people with fibromyalgia have underlying PTSD.

We explored Mary's childhood, adolescence, and young adulthood. She told me that starting in high school, she was picked on by the girls, and received unwanted attention from the boys because of her curvaceous body. This pattern continued after she finished school. Mary felt that she could not trust men or women. She was overly concerned about what others thought about her. This created anxiety, insecurity, and loneliness. Mary was afraid to be herself, and her self-esteem was poor. Since she retired last year, her fibromyalgia has gotten worse.

I told Mary and her daughter that PTSD caused her fibromyalgia. For Mary, school was a war zone. She went to high school day after day, only to be teased, ridiculed, and bullied. School was her world, and the world was not safe. To sixty-three-year-old Mary, the world still is not safe. She worries about what others think about her, and what they might say behind her back. She is afraid to leave the house, which makes her lonely and depressed. Mary has fibromyalgia causing her pain because she clenches her body at night while she is processing her anxiety in her sleep. In order to reduce her pain and fatigue, we need to treat her PTSD.

When Mary and her daughter heard my explanation, they both recognized the validity of my diagnosis. The story made sense to both of them. When I offered Mary medication, she started to worry about what her family would say and think about her. Mary, I said, that is your PTSD talking! You need to quiet your fears and use your rational brain to think more and feel less. That is what the medication is for. Mary agreed to try the new medication and to follow up with me in the near future.

Commentary

PTSD is lifelong. Mary had no idea that the patterns of thinking and feeling in high school were causing her emotional distress today. We must distinguish between rational worrying and emotional worrying. When we worry about concrete problems like our health, our job, or our finances, we are thinking. When we worry about hypothetical problems such as what people think about us, or what could happen to us in the future, we are feeling. Rational thoughts and emotional feelings interact to cause fear, anxiety, and helplessness. If this pattern is reinforced over time, it can lead to PTSD.

Some may think that the emotional trauma that Mary sustained was trivial, or even 'normal'. We must remember that it is the patient's perception of the events and the emotional reactions created that is more important than the objective reality. The more severe the trauma is, the more severe the resulting PTSD will be. While Mary's trauma and PTSD may seem mild to us, her experience was severe enough to cause anxiety her whole life. We cannot discount the diagnosis of PTSD because we think that the emotional trauma was not 'severe' enough.

<u>Mark, Age 35: War Hero</u>

Mark is a thirty-five-year-old veteran who works as a civilian now. He was in the infantry division of the army and was involved in combat almost daily. He was good at his job and killed many enemy fighters. He and his comrades would keep score of the daily, weekly, and monthly kill rates. It was a sport and it was fun. In addition, Mark could have been killed any day, but being in survival mode gave him focus and an adrenaline rush that he came to enjoy. As a civilian, Mark cannot reconcile the person he was in the army with the person that he is now. He came to see me because of anxiety, depression, and insomnia. He had gone to the VA and had been properly diagnosed with PTSD, but their treatment was not working.

My concern for Mark was not the usual feelings of PTSD—of being in a dangerous and unpredictable world. Mark feels safe and secure in his environment today. I sensed that there were two

Marks in conflict with each other: The thirty-five-year-old civilian Mark, and the younger infantryman Mark. The older Mark felt guilty and ashamed of his younger self. He not only took other human being's lives—he enjoyed the sport of it. I told Mark that many people who have PTSD regret the actions that they have taken in the past, but that it is not fair for the older self to judge the younger self. When you are in a hostile environment, you do whatever you have to do to survive. Danger was all around. For Mark, it was literally 'kill or be killed'. His actions saved not only his life, but also the lives of his fellow soldiers.

Mark needs to forgive himself for his past actions, thoughts, and emotions. He made a game of combat as a coping mechanism. His nightmares and flashbacks from his PTSD make it hard for him to forget. I told Mark that I did not want him to 'forget'. With psychotherapy and medication, we will work towards acceptance and forgiveness. The younger Mark did the best he could in a difficult situation, and no other person could have done anything differently to survive. His PTSD is improving, but it is a process that usually takes many months to complete.

Commentary

PTSD was originally recognized as a diagnosis because of the poor mental health of soldiers returning from war. This is what both professionals and nonprofessionals still think of when we talk about PTSD. We have failed to recognize that home or school was a war zone for many people. A person is in survival mode when they return to their toxic environment almost daily. Their emotional security is at risk. They are fearful, anxious, and feel helpless, day after day. This creates PTSD. It may be milder for a civilian than for a soldier who returns from combat, but the effects are similar. Now that they are older, they appear to function 'normally'. They have a job, a family, and a mortgage. Emotionally, however, they are struggling with insomnia, anxiety, and depression due to their PTSD.

Most people with PTSD want to forget about the past. In fact, they have been working very hard to suppress their memories for many years. They come to my office in physical or emotional distress, thinking that the past is behind them. Their PTSD is bubbling up from their subconscious and causing their symptoms. The treatment is not to forget the past. Rather, we must reexamine the events that caused the PTSD. We need to understand, accept, and eventually forgive our younger self for what they did or didn't do. They did the best they could in a difficult situation. As an adult, can they identify anything that a young person could have done differently to survive at that age? No. We need to reframe the trauma in a more objective and accurate way in order to give it less emotional power. What would you say to a friend if they told you a similar story? Why should you be less understanding of yourself?

Appendix B: ADD Stories

Steven, Age 15: Hitting a Wall in High School

Steven is a freshman in high school who is struggling with his grades. He had trouble last fall but attributed it to his getting infectious mono and falling behind. This fall, he has been distracted by health issues of a family member that are serious but not life-threatening. Steven failed two classes this semester. Upon further discussion with Steven and his mother, it became clear that he had similar issues with falling behind and underperforming in middle school. He was tested by a psychologist at that time for processing disorders, dyslexia, and ADD, but the results were inconclusive. No interventions were recommended at that time. Steven's mother states that his teachers know he is smart, and that he can handle the workload. Steven likes school, especially the after-school sports and the socialization with his peers.

After exploring the possibility of ADD with Steven and his mother, we decided on a trial of medication. I started him on Adderall with amazing results. When I spoke to his mother the following week, she told me that Steven had his best week in years. He was no longer anxious or oppositional. He looked forward to going to school each morning. He was finishing his homework assignments on time and was proud of his work.

Commentary

Frequently, formalized testing is inconclusive or unrevealing. When my clinical evaluation is suggestive of the diagnosis of

ADD, I recommend a trial of medication. If the patient has ADD, the response will be overwhelmingly positive, and the diagnosis will be validated. If there is a less than a WOW reaction, the diagnosis is in doubt. ADD medication slows down the thought processing, allowing the patient with ADD to focus and complete their tasks. The same medication will act like caffeine in the non-ADD patient causing hyperarousal and hyper focusing—it speeds up the processing instead of slowing it down.

I apply the same type of trial medication when I suspect one of my patients has migraine headaches. I prescribe a medication that only works for migraines, not for any other type of headache. Therefore, if the migraine medication relieves the headache, by definition the headache was a migraine. Adderall had a clear beneficial effect on Steven, so he must have ADD. Steven became less frustrated and less oppositional. His anxiety faded, and, for the first time, he enjoyed going to school. Both Steven and his family are benefiting from treating his ADD appropriately.

Carol, Age 19: Anxiety and Other Troubles at College

I got a frantic call from Carol's mother that Carol is at college and having a panic attack for the first time. She is crying because she is overwhelmed. Carol doesn't know how she is going to get all of her work done in the last three weeks of the semester. She is thinking of dropping several of her courses, or even dropping out of school. Her mother had never seen her daughter this way, and she didn't understand where this was coming from. Her daughter was always a good student. She has been getting all As and Bs so far at college. She tells me that Carol sometimes got 'moody' towards the end of the semester in high school, but she always performed well, and then calmed down during summer or winter break.

I said to the mom, who is also my patient, "Do you think that she could have ADD?" Her response was surprising, "You know, it's funny that you should ask that. I have thought that maybe she had ADD periodically during her school years, but she always got good grades, so I dismissed the possibility." This is a classic misunderstanding among parents and teachers. Carol got good grades in high school, but she had to work harder than most of her classmates. She spent more time doing homework, required extensions on reports and projects, and did extra credit work to compensate for her mediocre exam scores.

We gave Carol some Adderall and she was able to complete her semester at college. Now she studies more effectively, scores appropriately well on her exams, and completes her assignments on time. Her anxiety and panic attacks have resolved, and she is finishing her college career with flying colors.

Commentary

Some children are diagnosed with ADD in elementary school, but many are not diagnosed until college. When the student 'hits a wall' is determined by their innate intelligence, their compensatory skills, and the severity of their ADD. In spite of good grades, their self-esteem may suffer. Parents and teachers should be aware that if the student is struggling, ADD may be present even if their grades are satisfactory or even better.

A therapeutic trial of medication can help make the diagnosis, and the results can be outstanding if the student has ADD. Recognizing and treating Carol's ADD was literally lifesaving. Carol went from almost dropping out of college to finishing in the top ten percent of her class. More importantly, Carol feels successful. Her anxiety is appropriate and situational. She has not had another panic attack.

Nikki, Age 24: Never Failed A Test, Until Now

Nikki is a twenty-four-year-old nursing student who recently failed a test for the first time ever. She panicked during a recent exam and was unable to finish it. She came to see me because she thinks she might have anxiety, but she is not sure. I asked Nikki what she might be anxious about. She tells me that everything in her life is good. She has no situational conflicts when I ask her about her home life, school experiences, and friendships. I ask her about her educational experience prior to failing the exam. Nikki tells me that she graduated from college and got good grades in her first year of nursing school. This semester, her grades are not as good, and school seems harder. She does not understand why she failed her exam, and she is worried about her performance going forward.

I explore the possibility of ADD with Nikki. Yes, she spends more time studying than most of her classmates. Yes, she frequently forgets what she has just read. Yes, she is always thinking about several unrelated subjects simultaneously. She has difficulty focusing, unless she is in a quiet room with no distractions. No, she doesn't sleep well. Yes, she is a visual thinker and learner.

I tell Nikki that she does have anxiety, and it is caused by her ADD. I explain to her that her ADD is mild, and that she must be very smart to have compensated for it until now. You were born this way. ADD is hereditary. Does anyone else in the family have a busy brain? "Yes, I think that my mother may have it." Do you remember being anxious growing up? "Yes, but I could control it." Nikki, your anxiety comes from being overwhelmed. You haven't finished yesterday's homework, you haven't started today's homework, and how are you ever going to handle tomorrow's assignments?

Instead of being relieved, Nikki was skeptical and anxious about the diagnosis. She tells me that she doesn't think that ADD is 'real'. "So many students are being treated for ADD that it doesn't seem possible that they all have the 'disease'. In addition, my parents would never accept the 'excuse' of ADD for my poor performance." Nikki is a first-generation American of immigrant parents from a culture that doesn't recognize the prevalence of ADD and doesn't tolerate 'failure' for any reason.

I ask Nikki to trust me by taking a prescription for Adderall. I tell her that if she doesn't have a WOW, life-changing experience from the medicine, then I am wrong—she does not have ADD. I know that for Nikki, taking ADD medication will reduce her anxiety because she will be able to finish her work on time and won't get overwhelmed. She will be able to focus on her homework and exams, and her performance will be commensurate with her effort.

When I see Nikki one month later, the transformation is remarkable. Her anxiety is gone. She smiles when she tells me that I am correct—she knows that she has ADD. The medication is helping her focus, study, and pass tests easily. She has not told her parents about her diagnosis, but she no longer cares about their opinion.

Commentary

Nikki did not recognize that she has ADD until she came to see me. This is typical of many young adult patients I see. They make an appointment because they have anxiety that they cannot understand. The diagnosis of ADD is frequently a surprise to them. Once I point out to them how their brain works, and how it causes their anxiety, they are relieved. Their anxiety make sense.

Other patients were diagnosed with ADD when they were in elementary or middle school, but never treated. They come to see me because they are anxious as an adult. Many are successful in spite of not taking medication. They multitask well but have become overwhelmed recently. These patients do not realize that they still have ADD. I point out that ADD is lifelong—you don't grow out of it. Their ADD causes them anxiety now because their situation has changed. They can't focus on or complete the tasks at hand. These patients may need medication temporarily until their challenging situation resolves.

ADD is underrecognized and misunderstood by both the professional community and society at large. There is a stigma associated with the diagnosis and treatment, even though science has shown that it is a neurological condition that occurs in almost ten percent of the population. ADD can cause anxiety because it is challenging to get organized and to complete tasks. You are juggling so many 'balls in the air' that having one more ball will cause all of the balls to fall. You feel overwhelmed as you fall further behind.

Finally, adult ADD is real. It did not start in adulthood. It has been present since birth. When ADD is mild and the person compensates well, they do not hit a wall when they are young. When their undiagnosed ADD causes them to be anxious, they seek medical attention. We must keep an open mind when a patient comes in with non-situational anxiety: ADD might be the cause underlying their anxiety.

Karen, Age 28: Can't Finish College

Karen came to see me because of worsening anxiety. She is married to a man whose job demands frequent relocation. They move, on average, every three years. They moved here a little over a year ago. They don't have children, and there are no specific anxiety triggers at the present time. Karen has had anxiety for about ten years that has ebbed and flowed, and she has been on Ativan as needed.

I explored with Karen some of the possible stresses that can trigger anxiety but came up blank. Then I asked her what she does for a living. She said that she was taking classes toward a college degree, and that she worked as a bartender and server as well. I asked what she did before she moved here. She told me that she did the same thing. Did she go to college when she was younger? Yes, but she was unfocused in terms of a career or a direction of study, so she stopped going. What course of study do you want to pursue now? "I don't know." Karen has been 'taking courses' for over ten years and has less than half the credits required to graduate college. She still doesn't know what she wants to be when she grows up! What is wrong with this picture?

Although this was her first visit, I strongly suspected that she has ADD causing her anxiety. I prescribed Adderall as needed to help her with her course work. On subsequent visits, she reports that both her focus and her anxiety have improved. She is taking more classes this semester than she has in the past, and that has motivated to finish college as soon as possible.

Commentary

Karen is typical of many adults who did not finish college. Karen did not appear anxious, but her lack of focus and direction made her feel insecure. Her ADD is causing her to go around in circles instead of moving forward with her life. Now that she has the tools to finish her education, her life has more purpose and less anxiety.

Statistics reveal that approximately forty percent of students who start college don't finish. I think that a significant number of them may have undiagnosed ADD. Students with ADD can be underachievers if they don't receive medication when they need it. Our educational system is standardized: 'One size fits all'. Students with ADD learn and think differently than those who do not have ADD. Consequently, they are at a significant disadvantage when it comes to performance in academics. In addition, they may not be proficient in areas that require certain skills such as reading or math. They are likely to be visual learners and thinkers, and therefore excel in subjects that require spatial relations and pattern recognition such as music, art, sports, and trades (carpenters, electricians, and builders).

Unfortunately, our society overemphasizes the need and benefits of a college education and devalues those who don't have a college degree. Anyone who has had to call a plumber, an electrician, or a building contractor knows how misguided this is. I recommend that each individual try to understand their academic strengths and weaknesses, and then work toward a job or profession that utilizes those strengths and minimizes their deficiencies. Students with ADD are smart in ways that are not tested by the dominant reading, math, and science culture of public education. We need to recognize and value their skills instead of criticizing them for their underachievement in traditional educational subjects.

Christopher, Age 30: A Late Bloomer with Untapped Creativity

Christopher came to me because he was depressed. He is a college graduate who has had several unsatisfying jobs since graduation. He feels directionless. He is going in several directions simultaneously and is therefore going in circles. Upon evaluation, Chris has started many projects that he has never completed. He has great ideas and great vision, but he cannot follow through with the organization and attention to detail to bring his ideas to fruition. He performed satisfactorily in school but procrastinated and underperformed on his exams.

It was apparent to me that Chris has ADD. When I told him my diagnosis, he told me that his brother has ADD. I started Chris on Ritalin. The next week he called to say "Wow," the medication worked immediately, from the first dose, and it was life changing. He said that it was like a light switch turning on.

Chris got a new job. Within months, he received his first of several promotions. He sought out and discovered new opportunities. Chris eventually started his own business. When he started on medication, Chris began to see things that others didn't—the big picture, the possibilities, and untapped opportunities. He understood what his boss, and his boss's boss, didn't. Because he could focus on both the details and the big picture, he was able to visualize and create successful outcomes. We turned the negatives of his ADD into positives that were life-changing for Christopher. His depression and his anxiety resolved. He feels successful and in control of his business and his life.

Commentary

Chris is typical of someone who has adult ADD that had been undiagnosed in childhood. Chris is intelligent and resourceful, and he has utilized coping skills to succeed throughout his education. However, he hit a wall when he got out into the working world. When Chris was able to focus, he could finish his tasks. He felt successful. His self-esteem grew. He took calculated risks and was rewarded with success. His rational brain was in control of his emotional brain, and his anxiety and fears were quieted. Chris is successful and happy, and I am happy for him.

The more severe the ADD, the earlier it is diagnosed. Conversely, the milder the ADD is, the later in life it is diagnosed. When

ADD causes underachievement, anxiety, and depression, medication is indicated—even as an adult. The results of treating the patient are dramatic and immediate. The effect is frequently life-altering.

Jonathon, Age 51: ADD Affects Adults

I met Jonathon when he came to me because his former doctor retired, and he needed a new one. He is a healthy and successful contractor with three children, two of whom have been diagnosed and treated for ADD by their pediatricians. In talking to Jonathon, it became apparent to me that although he was extremely intelligent, insightful, creative, and successful by every measure, his self-esteem was low. He felt that intellectually, he should have become an engineer, not a tradesman, and that somehow, he was a failure. He was constantly trying to better himself to make up for his shortcomings. (What shortcomings? It was all his perception of himself.)

Since two of his children have ADD, I began to explore the possibility that they inherited it from him! He confirmed my suspicion that he had been a poor student, a procrastinator, and a visual thinker. Reading and bookwork came hard to him, but mechanical activities came naturally. I told Jonathon that he has had ADD his entire life. The decisions and choices he made were understandable and appropriate. He chose a career that maximized his strengths and minimized his weaknesses. The reason for his success is because of his ADD. There is no failure here!

I did not put Jonathon on any medicine. He now sees himself differently. His self-esteem is much better. He is now proud of himself for overcoming the challenges of ADD and creating a successful career that allows him to look forward to going to work each day. He is spending less time trying to do better and more time enjoying his life as it is. Jonathon now sees his ADD as a gift instead of a curse. He recognizes that he is successful, and that he is not a 'failure'.

Commentary

ADD is lifelong. People do not 'grow out of it'. Jonathon was successful by everyone's measurement, except his own. He was emotionally struggling in middle age in much the same way he did when he was school age. His response was to work harder to 'get the job done'. Once that job was accomplished, he became anxious and insecure about the next job. He could not enjoy his successes because he did not see himself as successful.

When I pointed out to Jonathon what I saw, we began to frame his life differently. I showed him that his ADD was a handicap in school, but a gift in his profession. I told him that he deserved credit, not criticism, for all that he has accomplished in his life— in spite of being born with ADD. He earned his success. He deserves the professional accolades, as well as the financial benefits that accompany it. When Jonathon began to appreciate himself, instead of criticizing himself, he became less anxious and even more successful—in all aspects of his life. Finally, this story illustrates two important lessons: People who have ADD can be highly successful, and not everyone who has ADD needs medication for treatment.

Reggie, Age 57: Great Employee Struggling with New Responsibilities

Reggie is an administrator at a retirement community. When he started working several years ago, Reggie was an assistant whose responsibilities included both hands-on functions and supervising other staff members. He is good at his job and was well liked by the staff. Reggie has been promoted several times and now finds himself in the top position of director. His new responsibilities include spending the majority of his time working on the computer and sitting through long meetings. Reggie is struggling with the administrative functions of the job. His sister was put on Adderall three years ago at the age of forty-six and said that it was 'life-changing'. Her daughter is in middle school and was diagnosed with, and treated for, ADD. She suggested to Reggie that he try it.

After hearing his story, I agreed to give him a therapeutic trial of Adderall. When I saw Reggie in follow up, he was a happy man. He reported that he could focus on and complete his computer work and could sit through his many weekly meetings. He now has the time to do what he loves to do: Spend time with the residents.

Commentary

Many people become aware that they may have ADD because a child or a sibling has been diagnosed with it. ADD is hereditary. If a child has ADD, it is likely that one of the parents does as well. If that adult comes to me because he or she is suffering because of the challenges of having ADD, I am happy to give them a therapeutic trial of medication.

The other lesson here is that ADD is more of a factor in the lives of adults because their professions have changed in the twenty-first century. Instead of having physical, mechanical, and hands-on responsibilities, many jobs now require more computer skills, conferences, and recertifications. Adults who have been working in their career for ten, twenty, or more years are now faced with these new tasks that are especially challenging if they have ADD. These people always had ADD, but they chose professions where it didn't matter. Now it is a struggle to keep their job. It is not fair to withhold the medications that allow them to continue to be successful professionals.

For adults like Reggie, medication may be taken on a prn, or as needed, basis. Reggie does not need medication every day. His ADD is a benefit to him in many of his daily activities, and he has utilized compensatory skills that he has developed over his lifetime. He is successful because of, and in spite of, his ADD. Reggie needs medication to perform some functions in his new job, such as sitting through long meetings. He now has the tools to do so.

Leslie, Age 59: Smart but Can't Complete Her Work

Leslie is bright, pleasant, and outgoing. She came to see me because she was becoming more 'scatterbrained' and was afraid that she might have early dementia. She had difficulty remembering simple things at work, such as turning off lights and computers, mailing forms, and copying documents. She had similar issues at home, forgetting where she put her keys, letting bills lapse, and not turning the oven on when she baked cookies.

I asked Leslie if these types of events were new. She told me that both her mind and her body had been in constant motion for as long as she could remember. Her friends were amazed at how much energy she had at fifty-nine years old. Her boss noticed that she was more forgetful at work, and that triggered her to make an appointment to evaluate if she had the beginning stages of dementia or Alzheimer's Disease.

I performed a Mini Mental Status exam, and she passed with flying colors. Both her short-term and her long-term memory were intact, and I assured her that she did not have Alzheimer's or any other form of dementia. I ordered bloodwork and a Cat Scan of the brain to rule out any underlying conditions that would explain her symptoms. Everything was normal.

Leslie told me that she was anxious, but there was nothing to be anxious about, present or past. Life was good. I gave her a trial of antianxiety meds. The Ativan made her calmer, but she didn't feel any better. We added an antidepressant medication. The Prozac made her worse—she wanted to jump out of her skin. I remembered that she told me that she couldn't sit still. She always had to be busy, and that she was that way her 'whole life'.

We stopped the antidepressant and tried some Adderall. Success! Her anxiety and her forgetfulness resolved. Leslie has had ADHD her entire life, but no one had made the correct diagnosis until now. She was able to compensate for her ADHD previously. Now Leslie uses the Adderall at work and is able to remember and finish her tasks. However, she takes it only as needed at home. When she is 'forgetful', she laughs and says, "It's just my ADHD."

Commentary

Anxiety is a common symptom that brings people to the doctor's office. Frequently, it is situational, stress at home or work. Even more frequently, there is no obvious stressor. Mild ADD that has been unrecognized can play a factor at any time in life. The anxiety comes from the inability to finish tasks; therefore, the individual becomes overwhelmed by the number of responsibilities that need to be done. Last week's projects are unfinished. This week's chores haven't been started. What am I going to do about next week's obligations?

Forgetfulness and fear of dementia is another frequent symptom that triggers a doctor's appointment. When a person is thinking multiple thoughts about multiple unrelated topics simultaneously, they may not be able to make a memory about what they are doing in the moment. The information literally may go in one ear and out of the other! They may appear to be forgetful. If they are not paying attention, they may not remember where they put the keys because they did not make a memory to recall. This is common when a person has a busy brain, in other words, ADD. Their spouse may complain that their mate does not listen to him or her because they don't remember previous conversations. It is not dementia. It's ADD.

By helping Leslie to focus by slowing down her busy brain, she is less 'forgetful'. She is relieved that she doesn't have dementia.

Leslie is busier than ever, but she is no longer anxious. She started taking Adderall at fifty-nine-years-old and it is enhancing the quality of her life. It's not too late for Leslie.

Made in the USA
Middletown, DE
17 August 2021